Ticklish

New ways to help your child Learn, Love & Play

DR JENNIFER BARHAM-FLOREANI

BACH. APP. CLINICAL SCI. / BACH. CHIRO.

Ticklish—
New Ways to Help Your Child Learn, Love & Play

ISBN: 978-1-4478-7302-0

Published by Well Adjusted Pty Ltd

Editing by Louisa Dent—www.elleldistudios.com.au

Design & Typesetting by BookDesignHQ—www.BookDesignHQ.com

For further information, please visit: www.welladjusted.me

Praise for Dr Jennifer

"Becoming a parent is the most exciting, fullfilling, yet challenging role I've ever played. Naturally, like all parents, I want to provide my daughter with the best possible environment for her development and allow her to shine in all aspects of her life. Having worked with Dr Jennifer Barham-Floreani for years, I've experienced first-hand how her knowledge and passion for vitality can change lives. My daughter was born premature and immediately Dr Jennifer gave my husband and I invaluable advice to assist our little girl and empower us as new parents... "Ticklish" is a must-read for all parents—wonderfully practical, chock full of the latest research on child development and written by one of Australia's best health authorities. So get tickling!"

Gorgi Coghlan (TV host, "The Circle", Channel Ten)

"Thank you ever so much for your dedication in sharing your wisdom with the world."

Dr James Sigafoose (chiropractor)

"We have been impressed by Dr Jennifer's balanced perspective... Well-informed parents make well-informed decisions for their children's health... and that means a better future for all of us!"

Dr Don MacDonald (author, chiropractor & speaker, Alberta, Canada)

"You can feel the fairness, love, consideration and wisdom from Dr Jennifer."

Dr Elizabeth Taylor (President, World Congress of Women Chiropractors)

"By shining a fresh light on health and encouraging an attitude of preventative healthcare and lifestyle choices, Jennifer inspires us all to do the best we can for ourselves and our loved ones."

Heidi Cummins (naturopath N.D. BaHSc. A.N.T.A.)

tick·lish [tik-lish]
adjective

1. **sensitive to tickling:** *children!*
2. **requiring careful or tactful handling and action:** *parenting*
3. **extremely sensitive:** *times have changed, it's a new ball-game and our children's developmental needs are different now.*

Tickling involves simultaneous sensations of pleasure and pain which can be real or imagined. Similarly parenting is a delightful yet tricky arena—particularly with the changes that our 'new millennium' children now face.

Ticklish discusses many new, simple, proven, research-based ideas for you to help your child learn, love and play, so that they thrive in today's challenging environment and express their full potential.

The 'tickle response' is mostly pure joy and vivacity...

...this is our goal as loving parents.

DISCLAIMER

Please read carefully...

This book addresses a number of health issues and countless published papers, articles and books have been sourced. Within the limitations of human nature, *Well Adjusted*™ has compiled these as accurately as possible.

The contents of this book, all text, graphics, images, studies and information are for informational purposes only. The content is not intended to be a substitute for professional medical advice, diagnosis, or treatment. Please do not disregard professional medical advice or delay seeking it because of something you have read in this book.

This information is not meant to prevent, alleviate, or cure any disease or disorder. Always seek the advice of a holistic-orientated physician, doctor of chiropractic or other qualified health provider with any questions you may have regarding a medical condition.

The purpose of this book is to compliment, amplify, and supplement other text. You are urged to read all the available material, learn as much as possible about health and wellbeing, and tailor the information to your individual needs. Every parent, child and family are unique with their own individual health needs.

Neither the publisher nor the author shall be liable or responsible for any loss or damage allegedly arising from any information or suggestion on this book or in any of the *Well Adjusted*™ products. Furthermore, if you suspect that you have a medical problem, we urge you to seek professional medical help.

Dedication

This book is dedicated to chiropractors who love their clients' children like their own and want nothing but the best for them.

A very special thank you to Drs Liz Anderson-Peacock, Neil Davies, Joan Fallon, Maxine McCullen, Simon Floreani, Peter Fysh, Carol Phillips, Wayne and Angela Todd, Genevieve and Rosemary Keating, Sharon Vallone, Jeanne Ohm, Glenn Maginness, Bobby Doscher, Claudia Anrig and Gregory Plaugher from whom over the years I have learnt so much on how to care for babies and children. Thank you for the clinical papers and the text books you write, and the seminars you facilitate, thank you for guiding me personally.

Thanks

My deepest thanks to my team—to Dr Kate Marshall for being my maverick research assistant, Louisa Dent for being such a committed, wonderful editor and Matt Cumming for bringing all of this content together so beautifully. Thank you for sharing the vision.

And finally to the fine gentlemen in my life— big and small—thank you for believing in me.

"Children come into this world ready to learn, love and play."
— Ingrid Bauer

Contents

The Amazing Developing Brain

Ways To Help Your Child's Brain Develop

—Tickles and affection

—Laughter

—Alternate sides when feeding

—Engage

—Carry your newborn baby in a supportive baby carrier

—Consider your child's head shape or head tilt

—Prioritize 'tummy time'

—Fire-up those antigravity muscles

—Give your baby objects to gaze at

—Encourage your child to have lots of 'free-playtime'

—Have your child's nervous system checked

—Massage your child

—Make sure your child is getting ample sleep

—Be active

—Prime your baby's senses

—Speak to them knowing they understand more then we realize

—Turn down the TV

—Limit their electronic time

—Know the milestones

—Minimize your child's exposure to toxins

—Go organic where possible

—Develop the habit of drinking lots of water

—Prioritize 'brain foods'

—A word on fish

—More 'feel good' moments, less 'out-of-sorts' moments

—Help your child develop a profound level of self-acceptance

A Note For Parents

—Your baby, work and the importance of time

—Environmental stress post-birth

—Poor sleep habits

Body out of balance—Toxins (Chemical)

—Exposure to medications, chemicals and toxins during pregnancy, birth and infancy

—Is the placenta a protective barrier?

—Everyday routes of toxin exposure

—Poor dietary habits

—Probiotics a critical step in digestive health

—When to start solids

—Allergies move a body out of balance

—'Poo tips' for adults and children

Early Signs of a body out of balance

—Newborn to 18 months

—18 months plus

Getting In balance

—Chiropractic care

ADHD

Proactive approaches to ADHD and companion disorders

—Nutrition

—Environmental chemicals

—Empowering behavioural strategies

—Tune the nervous system with chiropractic

—Medication

Autism spectrum disorders

—Autism symptoms

—Four factors to watch out for

—Getting support

Asperger's Syndrome

Foreword

As the mother of two boys, I know how divine and difficult the role of parent can be. I was lucky enough to have two beautiful homebirths, and in preparation, I read every book available about the birth process and felt very comfortable about facing whatever eventuated.

It was what came afterwards that was a shock. Sleepless nights, concerns that I wasn't capable, endless questioning about whether I was doing it right, guilt over the obvious evidence that often I wasn't, interspersed with overwhelming feelings of love and joy. It's an incredible rollercoaster that sometimes feels like it's never going to end. But it does, and getting the most out of your child's early years is paramount. Because before you know it, they're out of your lives and you're wishing you'd done more and shared more and taken more time to be with them.

Which is why Dr Jennifer Barham-Floreani's work is so welcome and important. Long acknowledged as a wonderful practitioner, in this book she succinctly and gently sets out how we can optimize our children's health and wellbeing outcomes.

Her experience is undeniable, her research impeccable, her advice easy to follow, but most of all, her empathy and compassion for parents and children makes *Ticklish* an essential resource for any parent.

What she writes about makes absolute common sense but often we are so bombarded by everyday pressures that common sense is the last thing that is in the forefront of the busy twenty-first century parent's mind.

As Jennifer says, things are different now, and the new paradigm means that we need to be constantly vigilant and thoughtful about how we raise our little ones. The first few weeks, months and years are the best opportunity we have to give our children a strong and effective physical, mental and emotional foundation, and the plethora of products and distractions don't help.

The recurring theme in Jennifer's book is joy, something which is easy to forget when we're surrounded by 24/7 bad news coverage. Children need to see, feel and experience joy in their own lives and in the lives of the people around them.

And of course, peace. We and our children don't get enough of it. But by following Jennifer's advice and being mindful of what we are responsible for and capable of, we can feel a sense of peace about our parenting abilities and the welfare of our dear children. And isn't that what we all want?

Enjoy your children and laugh, love and tickle them as much as you can, while you can.

Noni Hazlehurst A.M.

Noni Hazlehurst is a multi award-winning Australian actor in film, television and stage. She is widely known for her 24 years as the presenter of Play School, Australia's longest running children's show, and as the host of Better Homes and Gardens. She is a long time advocate for the wellbeing of children and has been the National Ambassador for Barnardos Australia, a leading child welfare charity, for the past nine years. She is committed to helping protect the lives of children who suffer from the trauma of neglect and abuse or the humiliation of poverty and homelessness, and she has been appointed a Member of the Order of Australia for her services to children. Noni frequently contributes to parenting magazines and is a passionate supporter of quality chiropractic care.

Who is Dr Jennifer Barham-Floreani?

Dr Jennifer Barham-Floreani is a mother of four, chiropractor—awarded Woman Chiropractor of the Year (WCWC, 2011) and Australian Chiropractor of the Year (2008)— and best-selling family health author.

Jennifer's work is respectful yet thought-provoking and encourages parents to define their own health culture. The material she presents is both informative and entertaining, written with heartfelt honesty and raw emotion that nourish the soul.

She is passionate about holistic parenting which she believes requires the constant sourcing of knowledge on how to nurture her children's health and wellbeing, strengthening their life force physically, emotionally and spiritually. Jennifer does not believe this style of parenting happens by default but rather that it requires both commitment and stamina.

Together as parents this enables us to raise a generation of conscientious and empowered young individuals.

*To see Dr Jennifer's best-selling book **Well Adjusted Babies**, as well as other products and free research articles, please visit www.WellAdjusted.me*

Introduction

*"The man who graduates today
and stops learning tomorrow is
uneducated the day after."*
—Newton D Baker

Today's parents are special. We have to be—we are raising children in a very different world. As the quote suggests, parenting today requires constant learning. And as my mother likes to remind me, "Things aren't the way they used to be."

She's right. Look around; they aren't.

Food isn't what it used to be. It's injected and sprayed (funnily, so are many of our celebrity idols!), our water is laden with chemicals, as are deodorants and sprays, clothing and furniture. Most of us feel overwhelmed with trying to keep abreast of modern lifestyle health threats. As proactive parents we need to be constantly sourcing the latest information and tools which may offer greater quality of life.

Prior to having children, many of us are so busy we forget to go to the bathroom, let alone contemplate what's important in life. Then along come our beautiful children and all of a sudden we want to invest in our own long-term health and fiercely protect our child's.

With parenting not only is there a huge learning curve about how to physically nurture our children but we then also want the best for them emotionally, desiring for them to grow into self-assured and socially connected individuals.

Most of us, however, are clueless as to how we can assist our child's brain development. We are unsure of what we should feed our children not to mention what on earth we need to do to strengthen their health.

If you too have ever wondered when you look at your child, "Where's the instruction manual?", know that you are not alone! Most of the parents I work with from across the globe have these very same questions and they have a similar goal to you in that they want to raise healthy, vibrant children.

Admittedly, I too have spent many anxious moments contemplating the enormity of parenting. The good news is there is so much that we can do to protect our children's health and nurture their minds and bodies. Babies learn to grow through movement and play, through their environment and experience, while children learn through being engaged in activities and repetition.

Overall the future wellbeing, growth and development of our children depends upon how well their bodies are functioning. The body operates as a whole organism and each system of the body is delicately interconnected. We discuss many topics in this book in order to arm you with a road map—not quite an instruction manual but rather a collection of ideas and knowledge on how to take your child to greater levels of health and wellbeing.

Ticklish discusses many new, simple, proven, research-based ideas for you to help your child learn, love and play, so that they thrive in today's challenging environment and express their full potential.

Some parents may have concerns that their child is not integrating their world well and again let me say, you are not alone. It is now estimated that at least 5-10% of children world-wide have ADHD and the number of children with developmental delay and autism is escalating.[1] According to a US research report by the *Greater Boston Physicians for Social Responsibility, In Harms Way: Toxic Threats to Child Development*, it is estimated that in the United States nearly 12 million children (17%) under the age of 18 experience one or more learning, developmental or behavioural disorders.[2] We have an epidemic before us and children within this spectrum, like any children, need us to believe in their potential.

I am not suggesting this book is a cure-all for any child or any particular health complaint, but I will point out that some of the greatest minds today had childhood health challenges and some of my greatest heroes are individuals who have defied constraints or labels that society had once placed on them and they have made a remarkable impact on our world.

Why? Because someone believed in them. Someone guided them, helped them gather tools and resources, and reminded them about the importance of self-esteem.

One life story that I often reflect on is that of Dr John Demartini.

When John was seven years old, his teacher sat with his parents and told them that John had serious learning disabilities and that he would never learn to read or write. The teacher went on to say that he would never amount to anything.

After failing year after year at school, at age fourteen John convinced his parents he could fend for himself. He hitchhiked around America, living off the streets, scavenging enough food and money to fill his days surfing. Then at age seventeen John almost died from a self-induced coma and at this time it dawned on him that he wanted to do much more with his life. A man then came to his aid who would become one of his greatest mentors.

John spent every day mastering reading and studying every field imaginable, including science, mathematics, astronomy and philosophy. He then went to college and found himself surrounded by peers who were asking for his coaching and assistance. He recounts one day that he heard one fellow student whisper, "That John, he's a freaking genius!" Hearing this, he began to weep.

Dr John Demartini has changed my life in so many profound ways and the lives of millions of other people. He is now considered one of the world's leading authorities on human behaviour and personal development. He travels 360 days a year to countries all over the globe, sharing his research and findings in all markets and sectors. He is the author of 40 books published in 28 different languages. He has produced over 50 CDs and DVDs covering subjects such as development in relationships, wealth, education and business.

His 38 years of cross-disciplinary research and study have led to much of his work being incorporated into human development industries across the world.

Throughout time there have been many people like John, known to have learning disabilities equivalent to today's ADHD, who have shaped our lives in many ways. These people include Einstein, Edison, Leonardo da Vinci, Galileo, Columbus, Beethoven, Picasso, JD Rockefeller, Eleanor Roosevelt, Elvis, John Lennon, Sir Richard Branson, Jamie Oliver, Will Smith, Presidents George Bush Senior and Junior, Michael Phelps and Bill Gates, to name a few.

I share this story and these names with you because each and every one of us—and each and every child—with or without a health label has a unique potential within them.

Your role as a parent is to love them and guide them so they have every opportunity to learn and grow.

My role as a fellow parent and health practitioner is to provide you with the latest and most holistic approaches to strengthening your child's physical, emotional and mental wellbeing.

And what an honour that is.

In fact I'm tickled pink

NOTE TO READER

For ease of reading in this book I make the distinction between mothers and babies by referring to babies using the masculine pronouns "he", "him" and "his".

"Nature never repeats herself and the possibilities of one human soul will never be found in another."
—Elizabeth Cady Stanton

Ways to Help Your Child's Brain Develop

In sharing a number of ideas on how to create a stimulating environment for your child, my intention is not for parents to become anxious regarding their child's progress or to 'push' their child along, it is rather to provide knowledge for parents who genuinely want to learn about their infant's world, to engage with their child and hopefully create a deeper, more interactive relationship.

Many of us lead busy, goal-oriented lives in which we race about, eager to achieve quick results and succeed in all manner of tasks, great or small. This cultural tendency permeates everything we do—even our nurturing. As parents, we may be eager for our children to achieve, and even when they are babies, we are encouraged to watch them closely, ticking the boxes of optimal development as they grow.

Panic may set in at the first sign of inadequacy, but although fears relating to autism and learning disabilities are sometimes well warranted, in most cases a child that learns to walk first is not necessarily Einstein-in-the-making, nor is the child who crawls last destined to be Homer Simpson. All children are different, they progress at individual rates, and neurological development naturally ebbs and flows.

While it is certainly useful for parents to have an understanding of developmental milestones, it is better again for them to:

- Learn how to enrich their child's environment;

- Appreciate which lifestyle factors may dampen their child's capacity to grow.

The Amazing Developing Brain

Did you know that babies have far more brain cells than adults? When a baby is born their brain has more neurons (specialized cell-transmitting nerve messages) than it will ever have later in life, giving the child an enormous capacity to learn and thrive. It is a baby's environment that creates the stimulus to get these neurons firing and wiring; i.e. the environment primes the brain. We talk a lot about this concept in this book.

I also find it fascinating that a newborn has their clearest visual acuity at 20–25cm. This is the exact distance between a newborn and his mother's face when he is attached to the breast. Equally, it is the same distance between a baby and his mother's face when he is being bottle-fed in his mother's arms. Indeed, each time your newborn baby gazes at you, they gain a sense of emotional security.

Furthermore, every time a newborn focuses on the same image (for example, his mother's face), his brain sends out nerve messages across particular pathways and synapses which help to hardwire neurological circuits into place. Every time he reaches for a brightly colored toy or listens quizzically to your voice, those synapses connect and eventually the circuits become strong enough to trigger a developmental milestone.

The first smile, the first time your baby picks up an object, the first time he rolls over or pulls himself upright on the furniture are all developmental milestones. Certain sections of a baby's brain will develop at different times; hence the age-appropriate time frames for activities or tasks will vary.

The questions parents often ask are:

"Why do so many babies today have developmental delays?"
"What can parents do to help nurture their baby's brain development?"

In this chapter we will learn how to enrich your child's environment and which lifestyle factors may dampen their capacity to grow.

THINKING OF BUYING A BABY 'BRAIN-TRAINING' DVD?

With parents being busier than ever before, it seems almost a guilty pleasure to take time out and play with our babies. You may be wondering, "Honestly, who has the time to get on the floor and crawl around like a child? Surely educational DVDs can stimulate my baby better then me?" Well, research suggests otherwise.

Interestingly, a survey of over 1,000 parents of 2 to 24-month-old babies[1] found that for each hour per day that an infant watched a 'brain-training' DVD, there was a significant decrease in the pace of language development. This was compared to the act of reading books with a parent; the latter was associated with a 7-point increase in language scores, while the DVD viewing was associated with a 17-point decrease.[2]

This research suggests that while infants learn quickly about their world by watching parents or caregivers, much less is learned when this information is presented via audiovisual media. The fact that the DVDs attract the attention of infants does not mean they induce learning. The American Academy of Pediatrics officially recommends parents avoid screen time for children under the age of two years: *"These early years are crucial in a child's development... Any positive effect of television on infants and toddlers is still open to question, but the benefits of parent-child interactions are proven."* [3] Indeed, there seems to be no adequate substitute for making time to bond and connect with our children. By switching on, we may be switching off more than we bargained for.

▶ ALL AGES Tickles and affection

A tickle is a touch that bursts.

As outlined at the start of this book ticklish means 'extremely sensitive'. I find it ironic that we can think of any child as *not* being innately sensitive. I believe we are all sensitive and aware until we learn *not* to be—until we become numb to our instincts, feelings and intuition.

Tickling involves simultaneous neurological sensations of pleasure, touch and pain which can be real or imagined. While there are different forms of tickling, according to Stearns it is the 'involuntary' component of this act that results in beneficial neural feedback.[4] Robert R. Provine, a professor of neuroscience and author of *Quest for Laughter* says that acquiring sensitivity to ticklish stimuli has been highly useful in our evolutionary past, for example, warning us if a poisonous scorpion was crawling on our neck. Moreover, the parts of our bodies that are highly vulnerable to injury, like our feet, chest and armpits, are among the most ticklish.[5]

Tickling can be a fun way to stimulate neural feedback. What I love about tickling is that it is impossible to tickle yourself. No matter how hard you try you can't tickle yourself. Quite simply it takes two and it is a beautiful reminder that our children need us—to guide them, support them, believe in them and parent them. So much responsibility is thrown on most children today that it is important to remember that we need to do all we can to preserve their childhood and avoid turning them into trainee adults.

How do we learn not to be 'extremely sensitive' or aware? By valuing commitments and schedules over being playful and spontaneous, and by valuing social acceptance and results over being authentic and lighthearted.

There is so much in life we can be serious about and by nature a stressful disposition affects our relationships, physical and mental wellbeing and our short and long term health. Our stress also affects our children.

What concerns me more is that children today face more physical, chemical and emotional stressors then any generation before them. These stressors begin in the womb and they have a cumulative effect. With this in mind I believe we need to do all we can to strengthen their constitution and empower them with knowledge and self-esteem. Times have changed, it's a new ball-game and our children's developmental needs are different now.

Research and our instincts tell us that human affection is critical for our wellbeing. Affectionate gestures such as tickling your child, hugging them, holding their hand, kissing them and praising them all affect their core physiology.

Many animals studies over the years have demonstrated that young animals will innately choose to be in an environment that offers some form of nurturing over an environment that provides nutrition, even if it is detrimental to their physical health. Here we see just how vital human connection and affection is—it is one of our most primal needs.

Tickling involves simultaneous neurological sensations of pleasure, touch and pain which can be real or imagined. This activity needs to be unanticipated and initiated by someone else for full brain feedback. Quite simply it takes two and it is a beautiful reminder that our children need us—to guide them, support them, believe in them and parent them.

By being affectionate with our children we help them feel secure and safe, loved and valued. This type of confidence allows them to be more self-aware and more aware of the world around them.

QUESTION FOR PARENTS

Do you dislike being tickled yourself? If so, consider why? Is it because on some level you have learnt to resist human touch? Does it make you edgy or frustrated? Perhaps ask yourself if it serves you to respond to affection like this? Does this learnt behaviour affect your parenting?

Are you over-sensitive to tickling and could that be due to a lack of human touch in younger years? Would it delight you to not repeat this deprivation for your child?

Now before you reply, "No, I just don't like being tickled because...", look at the questions again and sit with them. Then ask yourself, "How affectionate am I really?" How would your partner rate your level of affection? How long has it been since you stroked their cheek, nibbled on their ear or held their hand? Do your children see you as affectionate? Do you give random kisses and cuddles?

Sometimes we have the best intentions but as always we are judged by our actions alone.

Good food for thought.

Then ask yourself, *"How affectionate am I really?"*

EVENTUALLY OUR CHILDREN GIVE US 'TICKLE CUES'

Our boys are hilarious when they want to be tickled; they taunt Simon (my husband) and I with certain phrases they have learnt will result in being tickled—and of course, being young boys, the phrases are always testosterone based. They say things like, "Mum, you're not muscly!" or "Mum, you're not strong like me!" or "Dad, you've got man-boobs!!" To this we respond by chasing them, tackling them to the floor and tickling them until we are all breathless and exhausted.

At other times our boys may randomly approach and tickle us, a sure cue they want me to play. To this I reply, "Feeling lucky, punk?" or "Do you want a piece of me?" They grin enormously. Drawing out their anticipation, I very slowly move away from my desk or put down my kitchen tools, and then I chase them, wrestle them and tickle them silly.

The most wasted of all days
is one without laughter.
—*e.e. cummings*

A NOTE FOR PARENTS

Children with ADHD, autism and Asperger's syndrome may not enjoy light sensory activities such as tickling. Instead these children love deep pressure holds or moderate to firm holds on sides of their bodies; in fact they have a strong need for this type of deep touch stimulation which is also a form of affection. These children need you to persist with being playful with them, cuddling them, kissing them and holding their hand. Repetition helps them realise that being playful is important.

Please see related section, *Massage Your Child.*

▶ ALL AGES Laughter

According to Dr William Fry, associate professor of clinical psychiatry at Stanford University, who has studied the effects of laughter for 30 years, laughter increases the heart rate, improves blood circulation and works muscles all over the body. Fry compares laughter to "inner jogging" and claims that laughing 100 times a day is the equivalent of ten minutes of rowing.[6] That's a lot of laughing!

The point here is—a good time to laugh is whenever you can!

A good laugh and a long sleep are the best cures in the doctor's book.

—Irish Proverb

In *Humor: Its Origin and Development*,[7] the author suggests that when used skillfully, humour in therapy can:

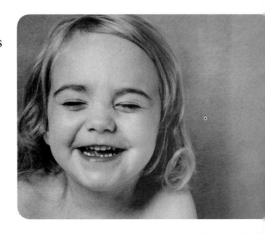

- Create a more relaxed atmosphere

- Encourage communication on sensitive matters

- Be a source of insight into conflict

- Help overcome a stiff and formal social style

- Facilitate the acting out of feelings or impulses in a safe, non-threatening way

These are wonderful points to consider, particularly with our parenting. Having a playful relationship with our children (free of sarcasm) promotes connection and feelings of safety, allowing us to be spontaneous and lighthearted. Laughter connects us with loved ones—label or no label. In fact, for developmentally challenged children, laughter is critical and there are many important physiological responses that are caused by laughter.

Laughter is credited with increasing the release of endorphins, a 'feel good' hormone which is the body's natural painkiller and protector against depression. Although the physiology of laughter and play are far from understood, we do have good reason to believe that the secretion of endorphins in the brain affects virtually every system of the body including, of course, our behaviour.[8] When endorphins are low, people feel anxious and they are also more aware of pain.

Clinical studies have shown that laughter decreases serum cortisol

levels, increases T lymphocytes and increases the number of natural killer cells. Put simply, these results suggest that laughter decreases stress hormones and stimulates the immune system.[9]

In paediatric hospital settings, unlike adult care, the use of humour has typically not been limited to patients with specific diagnoses; rather it has been used for all ages and stages of children and youth, regardless of the nature of their illness or reason for hospitalization because it has been found to be so beneficial.

Just as a matter of interest: People with low endorphin levels often have an appetite for fat and fatty foods, such as chips, cheese, chocolate, creamy sauces, margarine, butter and fried chicken, for example. After eating some fat, they will notice a change in mood, feeling more pleasure due to the release of endorphins. Exercise, by releasing fat from within the body, also raises endorphins and causes the same mood changes.[10] Isn't knowledge powerful? Next time you feel like eating fatty, nutritionally poor foods, choose to go for a run or a brisk walk instead. An effective way to beat cravings!

Carry laughter with you
wherever you go.
—*Hugh Sidey*

QUOTES THAT MAKE US LAUGH:

"Even if there is nothing to laugh about, laugh on credit."
  —Author Unknown

"Dad always thought laughter was the best medicine,
  which I guess is why several of us died of tuberculosis."
  —Jack Handey

"When people are laughing, they're generally not killing each other."
  —Alan Alda

"Whoever said 'laughter is the best medicine' never had gonorrhea."
  —Kat Likkel and John Hoberg

"Seven days without laughter makes one weak."
  —Mort Walker

"Laughter is a tranquilizer with no side effects."
  —Arnold Glasow

"Laughter is an orgasm triggered by the intercourse of sense
  and nonsense".
  —Author Unknown

"We do have a zeal for laughter in most situations, give or take
  a dentist."
  —Joseph Heller

▶ 0–2 YRS **Alternate sides when feeding**

Mother nature is so clever she has provided two breasts, not one, so that mum will naturally swap her baby from side to side whilst feeding. This ensures that even right-left brain development occurs.

Therefore, if you are bottle-feeding your baby, be sure to swap him from one arm to the other to mimic this phenomenon.

If you would like effective tips on breastfeeding and ideas on how to maximize the nutritional value of breast milk or formula feeds, please visit our website www.welladjusted.me and our eBooks (Chapter 16, Breastfeeding and Chapter 17, Formulas).

▶ ALL AGES **Engage**

First and foremost, the greatest gift you can give your baby is yourself—meaning your attention, your time and your energy. There are times when this level of devotion can be trying but in years to come you will delight in having spent quality time with your child; reading, cuddling, playing and building a lifelong bond and connection.

Like all babies, your baby has an innate desire to learn, to explore and discover. As parents we can help this process along with love and stimulation. It is the development of the sensory-motor loop (brain networks) that results in children learning to read, write and solve problems later in life.

Young children always model their parent's behaviour. If parents read books regularly then their children will be keen to experience the joy of literacy themselves. With the ever-increasing competition from technology, it is imperative that parents invest time in their children's literacy skills so that they might develop a deep love for this 'down-time' activity.

▶ 0-2 YRS Carry your newborn baby in a supportive baby carrier

An unborn baby spends nine months in the womb experiencing constant motion, warmth and physical contact with their mother. If a baby cannot feel, smell and touch their mother, this can be alarming for them. Researchers are now documenting the importance of the continued contact and motion on the neurological and emotional development of babies.

Baby carriers allow us to carry our newborns closely as we move about our day and provide a great opportunity for dads to bond and connect with their little ones. There is no harm in having your newborn baby fall asleep in these carriers; there is plenty of time to establish rituals around sleeping later on, and future sleep patterns will not be hindered with a few months of close bonding.

Note: be sure to pick a brand that provides good support for your spine while carrying the weight of your baby. As your baby grows larger (six months plus) it is wise to use a pram rather than straining your spine by carrying your baby.

▶ ALL AGES **Consider your child's head shape or head tilt**

There is a myth that an odd-shaped child's head is of no concern and will 'right itself' with time, however, anomalies of shape can be the first indication that your child is susceptible to developmental delay. A misshapen head is not merely a cosmetic issue; it is a brain stem issue. If your child's head looks uneven or you notice flat areas, this can indicate restrictions between the skull and the soft layers that cover the brain and spinal cord. A healthy brain requires good movement of the skull and spine; when this movement is impaired, brain and nerve function are also impaired.

Sometimes children have nerve and spinal distress that results in their head being tilted to one side so that one ear sits higher than the other (refer to picture below). At other times a child's head may be rotated or turned more to one side, so that they display a preference for having their head turned this way.

It is best—whether your child's head is odd-shaped or not and whether their head sits unevenly or not—to have their skeletal

SAMPLE OF MISSHAPEN HEAD

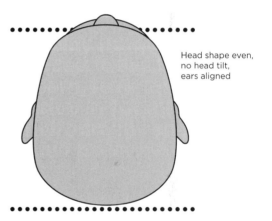

Head shape even, no head tilt, ears aligned

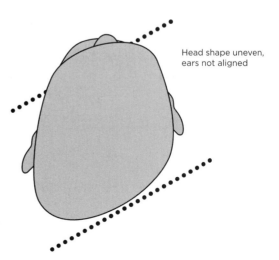

Head shape uneven, ears not aligned

system checked as early as possible by a chiropractor or osteopath. A chiropractor's focus is not aesthetics; their aim is to help increase the neurological function of your child.

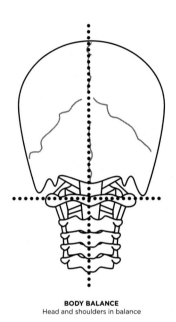

BODY BALANCE
Head and shoulders in balance

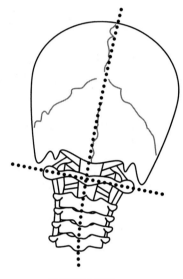

BODY IMBALANCE
Head sits unevenly on shoulders: most
likely spinal, nerve and cranial imbalance

"If young bodies are in bad shape,
what about the brains that
are attached to them?"
—Jane Healey PhD

▶ 0-2 YRS Prioritize 'tummy time'

From a neurological perspective it is vitally important that babies (from approximately three weeks of age onwards) start to have short bursts of 'tummy time'—time spent lying on their tummies and holding their own heads up. This simple act builds up their neck muscles and activates brainstem pathways which are critical for healthy brain development. For the first few weeks stay close by as a 3-5-week-old will get tired easily in this position.

If you lay your baby on your chest and talk to him, you will encourage him to lift his head and look you in the eyes. Also, each time you change your baby's nappy, roll him on his stomach for a few moments.

Note: If your baby does not appear to like lying on his stomach, this could be an indication of spine or nerve irritation, so have him checked by a chiropractor. Please also see Chapters 2 and 4 of this book.

▶ ALL AGES Fire-up those antigravity muscles!

Yes, our grandmothers were right, children need reminding to stand up straight; it is the 'tummy time' for older kids. With today's lifestyle, most children are neglecting to strengthen certain muscles as they grow and develop. They need to particularly concentrate on strengthening their mid-back muscles (the trapezius, latissimus dorsi and rhomboid muscles), triceps and their hip and knee extensors (squatting muscles).

It is important to stimulate the extensor muscles on the back side of the body as they neurologically fire straight to the cerebellum and improve the way their brain works. In essence, back muscle stimulation re-trains the static postural muscles.

Here are a few simple ideas and activities:

- Rub the back of your child's neck along their hair-line.

- Regularly tickle their back.

- Write letters and numbers on their back in the bath.

- Stroke their back through their clothes many times a day.

- Give them 'horsy rides' and 'piggy backs'.

- Play on all fours, pretending to be wild animals or fierce, four-legged dragons.

- Encourage cart-wheels and hand-stands.

- Dance! Use choreography to incorporate extensor muscle use.

- Play on jungle gyms, trampolines, slides and balance beams.

- Swing them around.

- Play hopscotch or other jumping games.

- Play board games on the floor with everyone lying on their tummies.

The back of the neck is the body's premier neurological and biomechanical centre so simple actions such as regularly rubbing the back of your child's neck along the hair-line will fire up their brain stem and the central axis of the nerve system. It also makes them purr like a kitten and feel connected to their body. I like to think of this activity as tickling rather than nagging the brain into action. It is such a powerful and loving way to enhance our children.

For more ideas, please refer to the "Be Active" section later in this chapter.

 Give your baby objects to gaze at

Babies love visual stimulation. As well as hanging mobiles you can provide wall charts with shapes for them to look at, ideally at varying distances. Start with black and white shapes because initially newborns see only in black and white.

Note: *if you would like to download free visual stimulation charts (one of which is shown here) please visit our Facebook page:*
www.facebook.com/WellAdjustedBabies

▶ ALL AGES **Encourage your child to have lots of 'free playtime'**

Babies spend nearly half of their waking time doing things like waving their arms, kicking and bouncing, and while it may appear all this activity is pointless, a baby is never 'just moving' or 'just playing'; every action extends the child's development in some way.

With this in mind, we need to allow children plenty of time to play independently. Although they may seem happy in a pram, a car seat, a bouncer or a seat placed conveniently in front of the TV, it is important that we do not 'containerize' our child more than absolutely necessary. "What's the harm?" you may ask, "It's a win/win situation, isn't it?" However, not allowing your child to experience the world around them can have serious consequences for their motor and cognitive development.

Whenever possible allow your child time to move about, explore their world and entertain themselves with a variety of objects, such as cups, balls, spoons, string, a plastic mirror, etc. Every time a child reaches out to touch something new their neurological synapses connect, eventually building circuits that are strong enough to trigger the next developmental milestone. As your child grows older, teach them to do stimulating activities like blowing bubbles or balloons, building with blocks, doing puzzles and counting beads.

Of course, beware the trap of trying to force your child to do 'constructive' activities all the time. Children need 'time off' as well, which means just letting them entertain themselves and initiate their own activity, whether that involves making something, reading, drawing or just daydreaming. It is important they be allowed to take initiative, to have unstructured time in environments which encourage their own form of creative activity.

For the young child, imaginative free play is especially important because it nurtures the kind of creativity which will be transformed into creative thinking. It is excellent preparation for reading, where written symbols must be corresponded with objects, actions and abstract concepts. When young children are using their imaginations in play, their brains are working and developing in a much healthier way than when they are being made to sit and copy pages from a workbook, for example.

▶ ALL AGES Have your child's nervous system checked

To maximize your child's nerve function, have them assessed by a chiropractor or cranial osteopath skilled with children. Clinical studies indicate that rapid growth of the entire brain occurs during the first year of life. Physical, chemical and emotional stressors impact the nervous system so it makes sense to ensure your baby's nervous system is communicating clearly and at an optimal level.

The Journal of Neuroscience (2008)[11] states that, although the first year of life may be a period of developmental vulnerability it may also be a period in which therapeutic interventions would have the greatest positive effect.

We discuss this concept later in this book; see "Why is my child not reaching developmental milestones?"

TEN REASONS PARENTS NOW TAKE THEIR CHILDREN TO SEE A CHIROPRACTOR:[12]

1. To maximize their child's plasticity (brain and nerve development)
2. To enhance their child's overall health and wellbeing
3. To strengthen immunity and reduce the incidence of colds, earaches and general illness
4. To help with colic and Irritable Baby Syndrome
5. To help with asthma, breathing difficulties and allergies
6. To improve spinal posture
7. To improve their child's ability to concentrate
8. To assist with behavioural disorders and offer greater emotional wellbeing
9. To help alleviate bed-wetting and digestive problems
10. To assist with sleep issues

Your child's health is their greatest asset.

▶ ALL AGES **Massage your child**

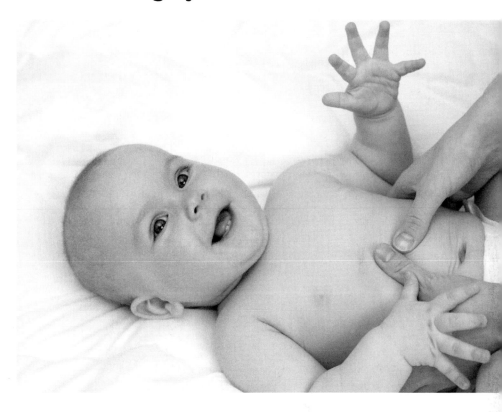

Massage provides wonderful stimulus and feedback to the brain. Please don't feel that you are not adequately trained to massage your child—even using simple strokes down the legs is a great start.

When performing all-over body massage, make sure your child is warm (after a bath is an opportune time) and use gentle, broad contact (i.e. use the whole length of your fingers rather than fingertips). If your child is irritable—particularly if they are over-stimulated when it is time for sleep—firmer pressure holds ('deep pressure' holds) are fabulous to calm the nervous system down. Use your hand to apply medium-to-firm pressure for the count of three and then move your hand slightly and apply the pressure again. Work slowly down one arm, across the torso and down the opposite leg to the foot. Repeat this on both sides.

▶ ALL AGES **Make sure your child is getting ample sleep**

It can be hard to know how much sleep a newborn baby or a child requires to remain healthy and alert. Please see *Poor Sleep Habits* for a detailed outline on sleep criteria.

If a baby or child does not wake up easily and with energy each morning, this could indicate they are not getting enough quality sleep. As parents we often miss our child's 'tired cues' and then we have great difficulty trying to put them to bed when their brain has moved back into fourth gear.

A set routine for dinner and bedtime makes life easier for everyone. Start these activities well before your child is likely to be tired and ready for sleep.

▶ ALL AGES **Be active**

Unfortunately today's little people spend far too many hours in highchairs, carriers, car seats and the like! Remember to let your baby safely explore the world around them and from an early age, teach your child a range of physical activities so that they can learn to balance and coordinate their bodies.

Activities like standing on one leg, hopping, skipping and walking along a beam or ledge (under supervision) are all helpful for balance, while spinning, swinging, ball games, clapping hands and cross-crawling (please see explanation and diagram below) all provide wonderful brain feedback and can be introduced early.

The action of cross-crawling helps to improve nervous system organization. The exercise causes the brain to reorganize and re-pattern, making sure both sides of the brain are firing well and communicating in a desired manner. It follows that the more a person needs to cross-crawl, the more difficult it will be to perform.

CROSS-CRAWLING TECHNIQUE

This brain-eye exercise can most easily be done when lying down or when standing...

LYING DOWN

1. Put both legs straight and place both arms down at the sides.

2. Raise and elevate the right arm above the head and at the same time raise the opposite leg, bending the knee.

3. Repeat procedure with left arm and opposite right leg.

Breathe in as the arm and leg raise, exhale as the arm and leg come down.

Once confident with this, you can turn your head towards the raised arm at the same time.

Repeat twelve times on each side of the body for a total of 24 movements.

STANDING

1. Place both arms down at the sides of the legs.

2. Raise the left leg, bending at the knee while raising the right arm, bending at the elbow.

3. Tap/touch the right elbow to the left knee.

4. Repeat procedure with left elbow and right knee.

Breathe in as the arm and leg raise, exhale as the arm and leg come down.

Repeat twelve times on each side of the body for a total of 24 movements.

▶ ALL AGES Prime your child's senses

Whenever possible, introduce new sensory experiences to your child. Let them play with a range of objects which have different textures, temperatures or that make different sounds. Use the everyday world to excite their senses; have them run barefoot on the grass or sand, dip their fingers and toes in water, or play with rustling leaves.

▶ ALL AGES Speak to them knowing they understand more then we realize

Just because babies and young children cannot articulate themselves doesn't mean they don't understand more than we typically give them credit for. Only using 'baby talk' to communicate does not serve your child's developing brain.

You can extend their lingual and comprehension skills using language; for example, as you put their socks on, describe the action by saying, "Give Mummy your foot and we'll put your sock on." Or rather than just pointing to a dog and saying, "puppy dog", you could say, "See the puppy dog, he barks and says 'woof, woof!'"

As your child grows, ask them questions that test their short and long term memory.

▶ ALL AGES Turn down the TV

Studies have found that 40% of households keep the television on 'in the background' and that this negatively affects children,[13] decreasing both the quantity and quality of parent–child interactions.[14]

If you want to keep the television on, turn the volume down as this keeps the brain active. It is also wise to limit the amount of television your child watches each day.

▶ ALL AGES Limit their electronic time

There is no doubt that children today need to be technologically skilled and that the appropriate use of electronic equipment has benefits for parents and children. However, long hours of unsupervised computer games can promote violence, competitiveness, addiction and apathy.

Our role as parents is to be clear about how much technological equipment we allow into our child's day and each family needs to set their own individual guidelines. As an example, here are some of our guidelines:

- Monday to Thursday: no electronics (except homework-based).

- Friday evening and weekends: any session has a half-hour time limit which is to be followed by some form of physical activity.

- No violent games.

- No eating while on the computer (we need to be mindful when eating).

THE DOWNSIDE OF TOO MUCH ELECTRONIC TIME

Our bodies reflect what we do with them. Spinal issues have been linked to the use of laptops, computer mice, portable telephones cradled under the chin and hours spent in front of the television.[15] Unfortunately, these postures place extra pressure on the spine and can lead to a host of debilitating problems including general tension and soreness, headaches, back pain and fatigue.

There has also been a marked jump in psychological (mental and emotional) problems triggered by excessive use of the television, video games, handheld computer games, MP3 players and mobile phone texting, especially amongst children and teens. Studies indicate that these may result in a myriad of mental health and sociological problems such as aggressive behaviour, attention difficulties, hyperactivity, schooling problems and other physical complaints.[16]

Poor posture influences our nervous system significantly, impacting how a person operates day to day and having an adverse effect on their wellbeing, overall mood and ability to concentrate or even work. When young children have poor posture they may be at greater risk of poor neuromotor development. Even small amounts of computer or TV time, such as two hours a day, have been found to increase the risk of psychological difficulties in children, especially if the child is not physically active.[17] Dworak[18] showed that exposure to TV or computer games affects children's sleep and deteriorates their verbal cognitive performance, overall negatively influencing their learning and memory.

▶ ALL AGES Help children through the milestones

The movement, behaviour and language your baby should ideally be demonstrating at different ages are called age-appropriate developmental milestones. Knowing these kinds of milestones can be a useful guide to help ensure your child's brain is wiring and firing in an ideal manner, and whether to take action if your child needs additional help.

Every child I see is like an athlete who plays a particular sport. Athletes all vary and I care for them in a variety of ways. No matter if they have a chromosome abnormality or if they can speak four languages, our children all have areas where they excel and areas where they lag. Our job as parents and carers is to compare them to themselves. ***Ticklish*** **uses the age-appropriate charts to map the evolution of the little person and encourages all parents to do the same. We need to have the courage to 'tickle out' the weak links as early as possible to prevent them becoming major hurdles in life.**

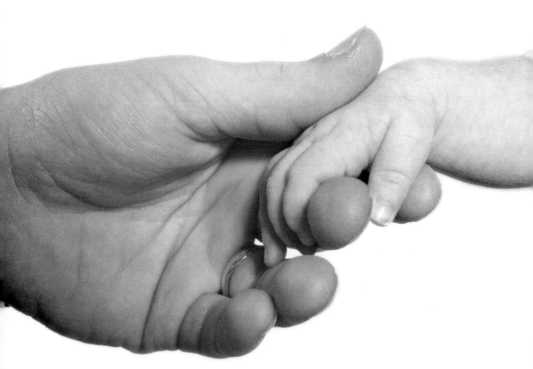

▶ ALL AGES Minimize your child's exposure to toxins

Pollutants in our modern environment—for example pesticides, heavy metals, herbicides and fumigants—have been linked to abnormalities in behaviour, perception, cognition and motor ability during early childhood, even when exposure is at so-called harmless levels.[19] Therefore, it is advisable for parents to provide their children with fresh air, organic food and a toxin-free environment.

In a five-year United States National Academy of Sciences (NAS) report entitled "Pesticides in the Diets of Infants and Children", it was stated: **"The data strongly suggests that exposure to neurotoxic compounds at levels believed to be safe for adults could result in permanent loss of brain function if it occurred during the prenatal and early childhood period of brain development"**.[20]

There are many reasons why infants and children are more at risk than adults, including: the foetus and infant have immature detoxification systems and the blood-brain barrier is not yet formed; children are smaller and so receive more concentrated doses of the toxicant; children consume less variety of food, so they might receive a higher exposure to a chemical contained in a favourite food; children play and breathe closer to the floor where contaminants accumulate in air and dust; children consume more food and water compared with adults, and they also breathe more air on a mg/kg body weight basis. The NAS report found that infants would consume up to seven times the amount of water on a mg/kg body weight basis than that consumed by adults. Water can be a source of exposure to toxicants for children, especially to children living in areas where groundwater is contaminated with pesticide and nitrate runoff.

As parents we can minimize our child's exposure to toxins by educating ourselves about the harsh chemicals found in foods, food packaging, furniture, toys and personal care and cleaning products. For further information on this topic, please see *Post-Birth ABCs, Chapter 14, Well Adjusted Babies (2nd edition).*

SOME OF THE CHEMICALS TO WATCH OUT FOR ARE:

POLYVINYL CHLORIDE

Polyvinyl Chloride is also known as PVC (denoted with recycling number "3" on the product). Health concerns surrounding PVC are related to both contact exposure (e.g. children mouthing toys) and offgassing (the release of the gas from the product over time). PVC can leach both phthalates (linked to hormone disruption) and lead (a potent neurotoxicant).

PHTHALATES

Phthalates are man-made chemicals found in personal care and other products and they pose potential toxic effects to the developing endocrine and reproductive systems. Phthalates are also used as oily substances in perfumes, additives in many personal self care products and in wood finishers. One of the phthalates, DEHP (diethylhexyl phthalate), has been banned in the European Union out of concern for children's safety.

Phthalates are not chemically bound and are therefore continuously released into the air or leached into liquids, which leads to exposure through ingestion, skin absorption or inhalation. Phthalate exposure is widespread and variable in infants. Studies have shown infant exposure to lotions, powders and shampoos were significantly associated with increased urinary concentrations of phthalates, and urinary concentrations increased with the number of products used. This association was strongest in young infants, who may be more vulnerable to developmental and reproductive toxicity of phthalates given their immature metabolic system capability and increased dosage-per unit. Interestingly this study also showed that children with the highest concentrations of phthlates in their urine had more severe ADHD symptoms.[21]

DIOXINS

Dioxins are produced as a by-product of PVC manufacture and are also found in a variety of household goods such as baby diapers. They are considered to be a global health threat because they persist in the environment for an extended period and appear to be very toxic. At even very low levels (near the level to which the general population is exposed) dioxins have been linked to immune system suppression, reproductive disorders, a variety of cancers and endometriosis.[22]

BISPHENOL A

Bisphenol A, also known as BPA (and denoted as recycling number "7"), is a component found in many plastics and the epoxy linings of food cans. Structurally BPA is very similar to oestrogen, the naturally occurring hormone, and there is evidence that it disrupts endocrine function in the body. It has been linked to low sperm count, hyperactivity, early puberty, obesity, small testes size and enlarged prostates.[23]

PARABENS

Parabens are widely used as preservatives in the cosmetic and pharmaceutical industries, as well as in food products.

Educate yourself about the metals and harsh chemicals that are in the everyday products such as prescriptive and non-prescriptive drugs.

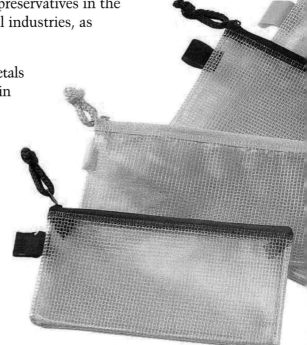

▶ ALL AGES Go organic where possible

Purchasing organic food is not a luxury but rather an integral step in securing our health. Organic food allows a child's body to focus on growth and development rather than having to combat the range of antibiotics, hormones, artificial pesticides and genetically modified organisms that are now found in generic produce.

MRI Studies[24] published in *The Journal of Neuroscience* on the human brain and its development from the birth to 2 years of age demonstrate large increases in total brain volume in the first year of life. Researchers suggest that this is a critical period in which disruption of developmental processes, as the result of genetic abnormalities or as a consequence of environmental insults, may have long-lasting or permanent effects on brain structure and function.

Without a doubt, if I asked you to choose between your child's health and any luxuries in your life, you would prioritize health. Having a child who is healthy, well settled and free from unnecessary chemical toxicity is surely worth any additional cost for organic produce.

REASONS TO PRIORITIZE ORGANIC PRODUCE

1. Organic produce is grown in healthy soils using a natural, seasonal cycle and safe, sustainable agricultural practices that do not rely on:

   • Genetically modified seeds
   • Synthetic chemicals (such as fertilizers, pesticides and fungicides) or growth regulators
   • Livestock feed additives
   • Antibiotics
   • Irradiation

2. Organic food has to be certified organic, unlike some health foods that claim to be natural and yet may really only contain 'nature-identical' ingredients (I have never quite understood this phrase—surely it is either natural or it

is not!). Look for organic certification symbols. Certified growers are thoroughly inspected and monitored for three years prior to certification and regular inspections occur at all levels of production to ensure standards. Animal, herd and flock welfare are held paramount with organic farming.

3. Organic methods help to restore and protect the environment of our planet.

4. Organic farming decreases the amount of synthetic chemical residues in our food and waterways.

5. Organic produce tastes better—another major benefit when raising healthy children.

I don't know about you, but as a child I do not remember arguing with siblings over who had the most zucchini or broccoli on their plate—yet, unprompted, my own children quite literally argue about their organic vegetables—go figure!

There are ways to make buying organic food cheaper such as buying fresh produce in bulk with friends and family and sharing the cost. If we consider what we may spend on packaged snack items, soft drinks, juices, magazines and other items that do not add value to our health, we generally find room for more organic items.

On the following page is a list from the Environmental Working Group on fruits and vegetables highest in pesticides.

A GUIDE TO PESTICIDE LEVELS IN COMMERCIALLY GROWN PRODUCE

RANK	FRUIT/VEGGIE	SCORE	RANK	FRUIT/VEGGIE	SCORE
1 (worst)	Peaches (highest pesticide load)	100	24	Cantaloupe	34
			25	Lemon	31
2	Apples	96	26	Honeydew Melon	31
3	Sweet Bell Peppers	86	27	Grapefruit	31
4	Celery	85	28	Winter Squash	31
5	Nectarines	84	29	Tomatoes	30
6	Strawberries	83	30	Sweet Potatoes	30
7	Cherries	75	31	Watermelon	25
8	Lettuce	69	32	Blueberries	24
9	Grapes (Imported)	68	33	Papaya	21
10	Pears	65	34	Eggplant	19
11	Spinach	60	35	Broccoli	18
12	Potatoes	58	36	Cabbage	17
13	Carrots	57	37	Bananas	16
14	Green Beans	55	38	Kiwi	14
15	Hot Peppers	53	39	Asparagus	11
16	Cucumbers	52	40	Sweet Peas-Frozen	11
17	Raspberries	47	41	Mango	9
18	Plums	46	42	Pineapples	7
19	Oranges	46	43	Sweet Corn-Frozen	2
20	Grapes (Domestic)	46	44	Avocado	1
21	Cauliflower	39	45 (best)	Onions (lowest pesticide load)	1
22	Tangerine	38			
23	Mushrooms	37			

You can also download this chart directly from the
Environmental Working Group website — www.ewg.org

BEST OPTION #1:
BUY ORGANIC FOODS AND
PRODUCE WHENEVER POSSIBLE

Providing an organic diet for your family is relatively easy as there are now many organic shops that stock a wide variety of products. Some fruit and vegetable shops, health food stores and supermarkets have organic ranges and they may also carry selections of organic baby foods. If there are times when you are unable to purchase organic items, please bear in mind the suggestions outlined in Options # 2 and 3.

NEXT BEST OPTION #2:
PRIORITIZE EVEN SOME ORGANIC

Go to the organic section of the market or supermarket and price compare—many organic produce items are competitively priced.

You can reduce the cost of organic purchases by buying fruit and vegetables in bulk. At the market for example, you may be able to buy a box of apples or zucchini, then cook and freeze what you cannot immediately use. Even frozen organic is a darn sight healthier for your children than the chemically-laden 'fresh' supermarket produce. Alternatively, you could always share the cost of a box of organic carrots, for example, with another family.

Organic food is nutritional dynamite!!!! I like to think of organic produce as a parent's secret health weapon. Even if you choose one fresh organic purchase a week, you can celebrate knowing that you are strengthening your family's health.

If you have to buy commercial produce, try only to buy those with lower levels of pesticides—see the Environmental Working Group's pesticide guide on the facing page. This produce ranking was developed by analysts based on the results of nearly 43,000 tests for pesticides on produce collected by the US Department of

Agriculture and the US Food and Drug Administration between 2000 and 2005.

NEXT BEST OPTION #3:
PURCHASE A 'FRUIT AND VEGETABLE WASH'

When you are unable to buy organic produce, the next best alternative is to wash commercial produce with a specific 'fruit and vegetable wash' and then rub them down with a 'fruit and veg cloth'.

You can buy fruit and vegetable washes in health food stores. These washes remove a large percentage of the chemical residue that lies on the surface of the fruit.

In my experience, these washes work very well but with heavily waxed fruits such as apples, you will also need a fruit and veg cloth which physically removes excess polishes. The company *Enjo* make a great cleaning cloth specifically for this task.

▶ ALL AGES Develop the habit of drinking lots of water

Water should constitute one of the single most important elements in our child's diet. Just as a car cannot run without gas and oil, water is important to the mechanics of the human body. In fact, all cell and organ function depends upon water.

A mere 2% drop in our body's water supply can trigger signs of dehydration: fuzzy short-term memory, trouble with basic math and difficulty focusing on smaller print, such as a computer screen.[25] Mild dehydration is also one of the most common causes of daytime fatigue. Many children are frequently dehydrated, suffering with concentration issues, constipation and digestive problems.[26]

▶ ALL AGES Prioritize 'brain foods'

Research has found that many patients with autism, major depression, post-partum depression, multiple sclerosis and cardiovascular disease are deficient in Essential Fatty Acids (EFAs).[27] Amongst children this is also a critical deficiency, with studies linking low blood levels of EFAs with increased risk of poor visual and neural development.[28] EFAs are vital to good health because they maintain the immune system.[29] A child's body cannot make EFAs so they must therefore come from the foods they eat. This is where the problem begins, as most children are literally starving for these foods.

EFAs are great brain foods and are found in cold-water oily fish, various oils such as macadamia and flaxseed, and egg yolks. These foods should only be introduced at age-appropriate times.

Please also see "Which Foods When" in the eBooks section of our website—www.welladjusted.me

SOURCES OF OMEGA-3:

- Flax and flaxseed oil

- Walnuts and walnut oil

- Pumpkin seeds

- Oily, cold-water fish that is FRESH, such as salmon, tuna, mackerel, bluefish, herring and sardines

- Marine or fish oil supplements, cod liver oil

- Soya bean oil

- Wheat germ

- Green leafy vegetables

SOURCES OF OMEGA-6:

- Many of our oils including safflower, sunflower, corn (canola) and soy oils

- Evening Primrose oil

- Sesame seeds

- Peanuts (small amounts)

- Peanut oil and olive oil

SOURCES OF BOTH OMEGA-6 AND OMEGA-3:

- Organic flaxseed oil (some brands also now claim omega-9 as well).

- Dried beans, such as kidney and soya beans (soaked and prepared at home—not tinned)

- Seeds

- Nuts (the most favourable being walnuts)

The most practical way to ensure your child receives enough omega-3 (some brands also include 6 and 9) is through a daily intake of flaxseed oil.

QUANTITIES OF FLAXSEED OIL PER AGE GROUP, PER DAY:

(can be taken orally, straight from a bottle or mixed with foods)

6–24 mths	2–3 years	3 years +
1 teaspoon	2 teaspoons	1 tablespoon

▶ ALL AGES A word on fish

Fish is an excellent source of protein, iodine, vitamins B, A and D, minerals and omega-3 Essential Fatty Acids. However, gone are the days where our only concern when offering our children fish was whether or not the fish had bones in it!!

There are now three major health concerns surrounding fish:

1. FISH HIGH IN MERCURY

All fish contain some level of mercury, which accumulates in the aquatic food chain as methyl mercury. In nature, deep sea fish require mercury for insulation.

The level of mercury depends on how long the fish has lived and what it eats. Deep sea fish or predatory fish (fin fish) therefore contain higher levels of mercury. Any exposure to mercury is a concern for our children.

The Food Standards Australia New Zealand (FSANZ) and the Food and Drug Administration of America (FDA) recommend[30] the following fish be limited in diets—especially for pregnant women, women planning pregnancy, lactating mothers and young children—due to high levels of mercury and its affects on the brain and nervous system.

FISH HIGH IN MERCURY INCLUDE:

- Billfish (swordfish, broadbill and marlin)

- Shark, or better known as flake

- Orange roughy, also sold as sea perch

- Catfish

- Bluefish, king mackerel and tile fish

- Oysters, clams and mussels have been found to have concentrated levels of mercury and pesticides.

THE FDA SUGGEST THE FOLLOWING:

- Limiting intake of albacore tuna to once weekly

- Limiting intake of low mercury fish such as light tuna, shrimp, salmon, pollock and catfish to 12 ounces (340 grams) weekly.

SAFER FISH OPTIONS

Summer, flounder, wild pacific salmon, croaker, sardines, haddock and tilapia. It is also suggested that molluscs (such as oyters and calamari) and crustaceans (including prawns, lobsters and crabs) generally have lower levels of mercury than fin fish.[31]

---

2. FISH MAY BE A SOURCE OF ANTIBIOTICS, VACCINES, COLOURINGS AND PESTICIDES

Salmon steaks, cutlets and smoked salmon may not be as safe as some of us would believe. Did you know:

- Farmed salmon are fed more antibiotics per kilogram than any other farm animal.[32] Whilst Australia's salmon and trout farms are free of most diseases, some salmon and trout farms use antibiotics, vaccines, hormones, pesticides and fungicides.[33]

- Wild salmon migrate long distances during their maturation, while farmed salmon are kept in cages and fed a high oil diet that may include pigments to give them a nice pink colour (producers can use a colour swatch called a 'SalmoFan' to choose a desired shade of pink).[34]

3. TINNED FISH CONTAINS THE TOXIC CHEMICAL BISPHENOL A AND OTHER NASTY ADDITIVES

Bisphenol A (or BPA) is a toxic plastic chemical found in polycarbonate plastic and the resinous lining of food cans. Tinned fish also frequently contains sulphur dioxide, sodium and potassium sulphites (220, 221, 222, 223, 224, 225, 228) as well as calcium disodium (EDTA, 385).[35]

In April of 2008, the National Toxicology Program raised concerns that exposure to BPA during childhood could impact the developing breast and prostate, hasten puberty and affect behaviour in children.[36] In light of these disturbing findings, please see the following section, *Tips to Minimize BPA Exposure*.

TIPS TO MINIMIZE BPA EXPOSURE

- Drink filtered tap water in preference to using unfiltered tap or bottled water.

- Avoid polycarbonate plastic bottles. Hard, translucent plastic marked with a number 7 is probably polycarbonate, which is known to leach BPA, especially when heated. Ditch your polycarbonate water bottles.

- Carry water in safe, reusable containers, such as stainless steel drinking bottles.

- Don't microwave plastic: use ceramic or glass instead.

- If you are formula feeding your infant, consider using powdered formulas packaged in non-steel cans. *Please see our website www.welladjusted.me for our eBook on Formulas.*

- Choose baby bottles made from glass or specially-marked safe plastics that don't leach BPA (such as polypropylene or polyethylene).

TOP FISH RECOMMENDATIONS

1. The best way to avoid tampered fish is to source a provider of organic fish; yes, that's right, there are now organic fish farms. Another option is to purchase tinned fish from manufacturers who use safe canning methods free from Bisphenol A.

2. If there are no organic suppliers of fish in your area, consider buying fresh local fish from the markets (not thawed) rather than the supermarket. Purchase the safer fish outlined above.

3. Large supermarket chains often import seafood, increasing the risk of higher mercury levels. Australian fish currently have lower levels of mercury. Buying fresh and buying local is your best alternative.

4. To attain the important nutritional elements of fish, you can try sourcing a supplementary, high quality fish or marine oil (DHA and EPA). Ensure the brand is low-oxidised and free of mercury and PCBs (polychlorinated biphenyl)—contact the manufacturer for their product analysis.

▶ ALL AGES More 'feel good' moments, less 'out-of-sorts' moments

Our body releases certain neurochemicals as a response to different experiences and different activities. For the purpose of this book, let's examine two 'feel good' chemicals, dopamine and serotonin, and two 'out-of-sorts' chemicals, adrenaline and cortisol.

It is important to know what activities facilitate the release of these chemicals so that we have less 'stressed out, over-the-top' moments and more 'happy-chappy, tickled pink' moments.

And that is always a good thing.

KNOWING WHAT INCREASES THEIR 'FEEL GOOD' CHEMICALS

When dopamine is released our body moves into an energetic state of bliss, motivation and focus. Children aged 6–9 have similar levels of dopamine to adults but during the teenage years, dopamine lowers—this may be one reason why they become lazy and cranky!

Bear in mind that 'feel good' activities have the power to change your child's mood, which is useful to remember when there is friction in the house or you are stuck in an awkward moment.

ACTIVITIES THAT PROMOTE 'FEEL GOOD' CHEMICAL NUMBER 1—DOPAMINE

- Being affirmed, rewarded or praised

- Being social with friends, interactive and playful

- Repetitive motor activities such as hopping, skipping, marching, trampolining, swimming, handball/downball, using a tennis ball machine or hitting a ball against a wall, table tennis

- Consuming good oils and brain foods

- Playing a musical instrument

- Getting ample sleep

The second 'feel good' chemical is serotonin, which keeps us from feeling insecure, lethargic, sad, frustrated and depressed. Serotonin has longer lasting affects than dopamine and again it is great to know what sort of activities help our bodies release more of this 'feel good' chemical. Artificial sweeteners such as aspartame and stimulants such as caffeine (found in soft-drinks and chocolate as well as coffee) compete with and deplete the body of serotonin.[37]

ACTIVITIES THAT PROMOTE 'FEEL GOOD' CHEMICAL NUMBER 2—SEROTONIN

- Plenty of play-time with no constraints of schedules or routine

- All forms of exercise

- Baths

- Laughing

- Watching funny movies

- Reading funny books

- Telling jokes

- Holidays

- Listening to music

- Dancing

- Feeling "heard" and valued

- Being affirmed, rewarded or praised

- Celebrating small and big achievements

- Affection – cuddles, kisses, tickles

- Ample sleep

- Family activities and rituals

- An active role in decision-making

- Learning new activities together with a loved one

- Removing nerve stress with chiropractic adjustments

KNOWING WHAT DECREASES THEIR 'OUT-OF-SORTS' CHEMICALS

The two 'out-of-sorts' chemicals are adrenaline and cortisol.

Adrenaline is mostly known for its activation during the 'fight or flight' response which enables us to act quickly in an emergency. It enables us to push through fatigue and to 'burn the candle at both ends' if needed. Excessive adrenaline can lead us to become fixed and focused to the point of detriment, where we sooner or later collapse from exhaustion.

Children with high adrenaline are typically hyperactive, highly emotional, argumentative, dramatic, busy but unproductive and maybe insecure.

It is best for them to avoid stimulating foods and beverages containing colours, preservatives, additives, caffeine or sugar. Adrenaline is also increased by violent or competitive activities, such as some computer games. Parents can provide a living environment that has safe and loving boundaries, and teach them how to behave and interact in a manner that is safe and appropriate.

ACTIVITIES THAT *INCREASE* 'OUT-OF-SORTS' CHEMICAL NUMBER 1—ADRENALINE

- Arguing

- Violent or competitive activities

- Too many commitments, engagements and a tight schedule

- Dehydration

- Foods high in sugar, caffeine and additives

ACTIVITIES THAT *DECREASE* 'OUT-OF-SORTS' CHEMICAL NUMBER 1—ADRENALINE

- Scheduling some rituals that promote organization, such as keeping a calendar of up-and-coming events or having an end-of week clean up of bedrooms.

- Being listened to

- One-on-one quality time

- Calm, proactive communication

The second 'out-of-sorts' chemical is cortisol, which is produced at the same time as adrenaline whenever the body is fired up. Cortisol is the body's 'stress' hormone. Have you ever noticed that when a child becomes agitated or angry they can't speak well and instead they tend to lash out physically—this is because the cortisol literally shuts down the language centre of the brain.

When stressed our high cortisol levels prevent us from prioritizing or thinking clearly and we become easily upset and reactive. In fact, moodiness, anxiety and depression are all consequences of long-term elevation of cortisol and decreased levels of serotonin and dopamine.

When we allow ourselves to be chronically stressed our blood sugar levels elevate, as does our appetite and so we crave sweet, calorie-dense foods and salty, high carbohydrate snacks. These foods are typically full of additives which exacerbates the problem. Our immune system also becomes weary after long periods of elevated stress so we need to focus on building up the body's constitution.

ACTIVITIES THAT *INCREASE* 'OUT-OF-SORTS' CHEMICAL NUMBER 2—CORTISOL

- Fluorescent lighting

- Lack of fresh air

- Fatigue

- Dehydration

ACTIVITIES THAT *DECREASE* 'OUT-OF-SORTS' CHEMICAL NUMBER 2—CORTISOL

- Talking about worries and concerns

- Getting physical

- Walking barefoot on the grass, relaxing in the sunshine

- Breathing deeply

- Drinking lots of water

- Avoiding foods and beverages containing stimulants

- Trading carbohydrate snacks for real foods that are protein based or fruits and vegetables

- Building up their immune system with multi-mineral powders, probiotics and B vitamins

- Getting plenty of sleep

- Laughter

Being tickled is the fastest way to connect your heart to your head, to experience sense and nonsense.

—Dr Simon Floreani

▶ ALL AGES Help your child develop a profound level of self-acceptance

Another extremely valuable gift we can offer our children is an authentic belief in themselves. A baby is intimately attuned to their caregiver's feelings, so as parents we need to be mindful of sending them the message that they are unconditionally lovable. Whenever you are delighted and pleased with your baby's behaviour or capacity to try something new and to learn, let them know! As they grow older, tell them how amazing and clever they are. Aim to 'talk them up and build them up' and to reduce criticism as much as possible. Tell them you believe in them and give them permission to shine and be wonderful.

If we make time to play and chat then we demonstrate through our behaviour that we value them and our relationship with them, above and beyond the demands of our careers or other affairs. If we genuinely enjoy their company and value their thoughts and opinions, they will grow up knowing they are important and appreciated.

When I first had children I naively thought I would have eighteen years to shape and mould their values and life philosophies. What I didn't realize is that while children may dwell with us for what seems like eternity, they tune out to our intentions and desires a lot sooner then we may like. By the time they are eight years old, children begin to weigh up their parents' opinions against those of other adults and by the time they are thirteen, parents have to work extra hard at listening to their children so that their children will want to listen to them. At this age they are far more interested in the opinions of their peers.

In his book *The People Puzzle*,[38] sociologist Dr Morris Massey described three major periods during which values are developed. They are as follows:

1.   THE IMPRINT PERIOD

Up to the age of seven, children are like sponges, absorbing everything around them and accepting much of it as true, especially when it comes from their parents.

2.   THE MODELLING PERIOD

Between the ages of 8-13, children copy people, often their parents, but also other people that are important in their lives.

3.   THE SOCIALIZATION PERIOD

Between the ages of 13-21, children are largely influenced by their peers. As they develop into individuals and look for ways to get away from their earlier programming, they naturally turn to people who seem more like them. Other influences include media, especially those aspects that seem to resonate with the values of the peer group.

This outline helps us realize how our children are influenced by people and the world around them.

A note for parents: **your child, work and the importance of 'time'**

Have you been reading the suggestions so far in this book and wondering how you can balance life and work better? Are you reassessing your current work commitments or have you just had a newborn and are wondering when to return to work?

In his study "Affect Regulation and the Origin of Self",[39] Dr Schore explains that, "Science now tells us, without a shadow of a doubt, that a mother's constant contact actually helps form a baby's brain and create intricate connections which will determine his or her wellbeing and sense of self for the remainder of his or her life."

At the World Congress of Families III, the President for Alliance for Family cited studies[40] which demonstrate that the cerebral cortex of the human brain does not grow automatically. It requires stimulation in its main growth phase, i.e. the first six years of life. "That is why children who learn languages or learn to ski at an early age will learn these tasks easily. The cortex adapts to the demands of stimulation and neurons are produced to respond to these." She adds, "More importantly though is the development of our limbic system, which is the part of the brain that governs the sense of self, emotions and a host of elements of a balanced and happy individual. The main development of the limbic system takes place in the first four years."

As your baby and family grow, you will face hundreds of decisions—although none of these decisions is more important than prioritizing how much time you should spend with your child. As a parent, only you can decide what is appropriate for your family and your decisions may also vary at different times in your life.

SOME PARENTAL DECISIONS INCLUDE:

• Should I go back to work?

• Would my partner be better to stay at home?

• How much should I work?

• Should we use crèche or day care?

• When should my child go to kindergarten?

• Should we use after-school care?

When a baby comes along, there are so many changes to our daily routine that can make the rituals of our previous life seem like sheer luxuries. Life can be extremely chaotic while we learn to master new skills and it is often easier and more beneficial to surrender and embrace these new priorities than to resist such change. Children have many needs yet perhaps their greatest need is simplicity. Children remind us there can be great pleasure in slowing down our daily haste.

Some parenting books discuss the benefits of children under the age of two being constantly near their mothers and not being apart for more than a couple of hours at a time. These parental guidelines, while meritorious, can seem quite stern. Furthermore, if a mother is unhappy at home (for whatever reason) then this could also be reflected in her relationship with her child. Put in perspective, this scenario may not be feasible for many families.

Other books suggest that if a mother wants or needs to work, the best option for a carer is another family member, such as a grandparent or aunt. They also suggest that the carer ideally be located close to the mother so that she is accessible for feeds. Alternatively, some authors discuss the benefits of leaving children in a 'home care' scenario where another mother cares for a group of children in her own home. Crèches are often considered the final option due to the sheer number of children present and the inconsistency of carers.

If a parent wants to work or has to work, they will need lots of energy to organize and create extra time with their child. This does not mean choosing activities that over-stimulate their child just because they are home but rather focusing on quality, one-on-one time. Rather than trying to complete a multitude of tasks with your child in tow, choose to read, cuddle, be creative and re-learn the art of playing.

As a parent, you will probably find that whatever you decide to do in relation to nurturing your child will raise eyebrows. I now look at this antagonism as an opportunity to assess how strongly I really feel about my choices. Clarity is a wonderful thing.

Follow your heart and remember that as a parent we do not get back these 'wonder years' so be creative with your work and life balance.

Laughter is an instant vacation.
—Milton Berle

*Children remind us
there can be great pleasure in
slowing down our daily haste.*

Milestones for the New Millennium Child

The developmental milestones outlined in the following charts indicate the age when most babies undergo these changes. They are meant as a guide only and are not gender-specific.

Every child I see is like an athlete who plays a particular sport. Athletes all vary and I care for them in a variety of ways. No matter if they have a chromosome abnormality or if they can speak four languages, our children all have areas where they excel and areas where they lag. Our job as parents and carers is to compare them to themselves. *Ticklish* uses the age-appropriate charts to map the evolution of the little person and encourages all parents to do the same. We need to have the courage to 'tickle out' the weak links as early as possible to prevent them becoming major hurdles in life.

2

Birth to 8 weeks

◉ VISION

☐ Your newborn will have blurred vision for the first week because the centre of the eye—the part that sees colour—has not yet developed.

☐ Your baby sees most clearly at a distance of 20–25 cm, which is about the distance that a newborn focuses on his mother when breastfeeding.

☐ Newborns like toys with bold bright colors or stark contrast, like black and white.

☐ Your baby will have long spells of staring vacantly at large masses (walls, windows).

☐ After about a month, pupils will be sensitive to changes in brightness and your baby will turn his head toward sudden bright light.

☐ After four weeks your baby will focus on the face of whomever is holding him, and he may follow a toy if you move it in an arc-like motion.

Grasping is one of the most important functions that influence the total development of your baby."

📶 HEARING

☐ Your baby will recognize your voice and smell.

☐ Your baby will be startled by loud noises.

☐ After four weeks he will show interest in voices and begin to recognize yours.

☐ At four weeks your baby will have different cries and will respond to soothing voices.

⚙ MOTOR

Your baby will usually display the following important reflexes:

☐ Rooting reflex – touch a newborn's face and he will turn towards you, opening his mouth and searching for something to suck.

☐ Grasping reflex – up until about eight weeks, if you put your little finger in his hand, he will hold it tightly.

☐ Suckling reflex – if something enters his mouth, he will lower his tongue to create a vacuum and then begin to suck.

☐ Walking reflex – if he is held upright and his feet touch the floor, he will make walking movements.

☐ Moro/startle reflex – if you hold his body without supporting his limbs, he will throw out his limbs and arch his back, then bring himself into foetal position.

☐ Within four weeks he is able to hold his head up momentarily from the changing table.

⊞ SUGGESTIONS

From Birth

- Alternate your baby from side to side whilst feeding — this ensures that even right-left brain development occurs. Swap sides even when bottle-feeding.

- Look your baby in the eyes and talk to him frequently throughout the day.

- Get skin-to-skin contact with your baby as often as you can.

- Blow 'raspberries' on his tummy.

- Massage your baby, as massage provides wonderful stimulus and feedback to the brain.

- Have your baby's nervous system checked by a chiropractor or cranial osteopath skilled with children. Constraint in the uterus or via the birth process can impair nerve function. The earlier your baby is checked the better.

From 3 weeks

- When changing his nappy turn him onto his tummy and briefly (10 seconds) let him lie there; this encourages him to support the weight of his head.

- Lay your baby on your chest and talk to him, encouraging him to lift his head and look you in the eyes.

  (If your baby does not appear to like lying on their stomach, this could be an indication of spine or nerve irritation and it is best to have them checked by a chiropractor).

- Babies love visual stimulation. Hang mobiles and wall charts with shapes for them to look at, ideally at varying distances. Start with black and white shapes.

From 6 weeks

- Continue putting your baby on his tummy each time you change his nappy, slowing increasing the time to 30 seconds.

- Lie on the floor with him so he has to lift up his head to see you.

- Hold him in your arms and whilst supporting his neck, bend your legs up and down (as if simulating an elevator). Alternatively, hold him safely whilst rocking to and fro in a rocking chair, or place him on your knees whilst sitting on a swivel chair, turning round and round. These motions are said to stimulate production of new brain cells and synapses.

- Introduce colour and slightly more complex patterns to your baby's field of vision.

- Cover a torch with different coloured cloths or pieces of cellophane and move it from side to side to see if he will track it.

CARRY YOUR BABY IN SUPPORTIVE BABY CARRIERS AS MUCH AS POSSIBLE.

An unborn baby spends nine months in the womb experiencing constant motion, warmth, and physical contact with the mother. If a baby cannot feel, smell, and touch their mother, this can be alarming for them and neurological development is often impaired under stressful situations. Researchers are now recognizing the importance of continued contact and motion on the neurological and emotional development of babies.

From 8 weeks

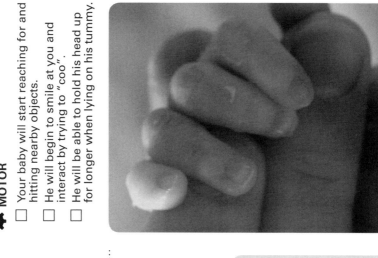

◉ VISION

- [ ] Your baby will begin to focus intently on his hands and other objects that are put in front of him.
- [ ] He will begin to recognize your face.
- [ ] He will have greater depth perception.

📶 HEARING

- [ ] Your baby will like to listen to musical sounds.
- [ ] He will begin to recognize your voice.

⚙ MOTOR

- [ ] Your baby will start reaching for and hitting nearby objects.
- [ ] He will begin to smile at you and interact by trying to "coo".
- [ ] He will be able to hold his head up for longer when lying on his tummy.

⊣⊢ SUGGESTIONS

- Continue putting him on his tummy each time you change his nappy, slowing increasing the time interval.
- Lie on the floor with him so he has to lift up his head to see you.
- Shake rattles and toys that attract his attention and encourage him to follow the sound with his eyes.

SAFE PLASTIC TOYS?

Minimize your child's exposure to toxins by educating yourself about the harsh chemicals found in many plastic products including baby's toys.

Watch out for the poison plastic PVC which can leach phthalates (linked to hormone disruption) and lead (a potent neurotoxicant). Health concerns surrounding PVC are related to both contact exposure (e.g. children putting toys in their mouths) and offgassing.

Go PVC-free by reading packages and avoiding the recycling classification number 3 (found in the 'chasing arrows' symbol on the bottom of a product).

Also be mindful of Bisphenol A (BPA), a component in plastics.

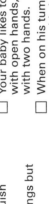

From 12 weeks

 VISION

- [ ] Your baby will start to recognize faces and places.
- [ ] He will be able to distinguish between colours.
- [ ] Your baby reaches for things but misses.
- [ ] He will watch his hands.

MOTOR

- [ ] Your baby will put objects in his mouth.
- [ ] Your baby likes to reach and feel with open hands, grasping crudely with two hands.
- [ ] When on his tummy, his forearms can support his head and shoulders.
- [ ] Ideally, he should be starting to roll himself over.

SUGGESTIONS

- With your hand, gently cover one of your baby's eyes, then shine a small light across the open eye and notice if the pupil of his eye constricts or becomes smaller. Just test this once or twice — do not do repeatedly.
- From around 3-4 months, if you clap your hands near your baby's head he will not have such a big startle response.
- Place your baby on his tummy and when he extends one arm forward to touch an object, see if the opposite leg bends up to push off with the toe. If not, then gently bend up this knee to stimulate the cross-over of brain pathways.

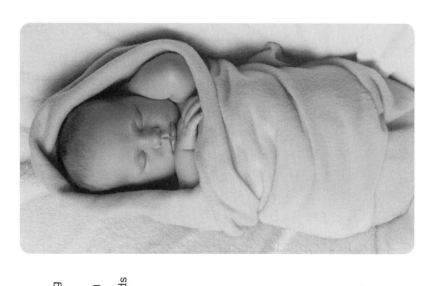

4 months

MOTOR

- [ ] He likes to grasp things, then let go and kick at the same time.
- [ ] He holds and shakes a rattle which is placed in his hand.
- [ ] He plays with his own hands.
- [ ] Ideally, he should be rolling from side to side.

COMMUNICATION

- [ ] Your baby is laughing and blowing 'raspberries'.
- [ ] He has learnt that language is fun and is constantly making babbling sounds.
- [ ] He will laugh at unexpected sounds and sights, and loves games like 'peek-a-boo'.

Babies spend nearly half of their waking time doing things like waving their arms, kicking and bouncing. And while it may appear all this activity is just for the sake of moving, it's important to realize a baby is never 'just moving' or 'just playing'. Every action extends the child's development in some way.

5 months

VISION

- [ ] Your baby will start to make longer eye contact and explore your face.
- [ ] His peripheral vision develops.

COMMUNICATION

- [ ] He uses one syllable words, such as "ah" and "da".
- [ ] Be aware he may be shy around strangers.

MOTOR

- [ ] Your baby will be grasping objects and transferring them from one hand to the other.
- [ ] You can gently pull him into a sitting position while he is lying on his back.
- [ ] When on his back, he may push up with his legs, lifting his bottom.
- [ ] He discovers his feet.
- [ ] When lying on his stomach, he pushes up with his arms.
- [ ] He plays actively when propped up with cushions in a play area for 10-15 minutes.
- [ ] He likes to stand up in your lap and push up on his feet.
- [ ] He likes to bang items.

SUGGESTIONS

- Give your baby a range of toys and objects, including those that make noise.
- Allow your baby time to move about, explore his world and entertain himself with a variety of objects such as cups, soft balls, plastic spoons (BPA-free), string, a plastic mirror, etc.
- Give him a rubber suction toy on the tray of his high chair.
- Put a few 'pop-up' toys within easy reach. Watch his surprise as he hits the right buttons.
- Play 'peek-a-boo'.
- Show him 'lift-the-flap' cloth books.
- Let him look at his reflection in a mirror.

6 months

VISION

- [ ] Your baby develops greater form perception and has an ability to know object shapes and sizes.
- [ ] He is able to recognize familiar faces.

MOTOR

- [ ] Your baby can roll over, lift his head and shoulders when lying on his back, and raise his arms to be picked up.
- [ ] He may be able to sit up unsupported for a brief time.
- [ ] He can move an object from one hand to the other.
- [ ] He examines objects by placing them in his mouth; he likes to chew them.
- [ ] When lying on his stomach, his head and upper body can be supported by his hands and arms.
- [ ] He may try to pivot in a semi-circle on his tummy in search of toys.
- [ ] He likes to play with his feet.
- [ ] He likes to shake objects and bang objects down.
- [ ] He may hold onto a bottle.

COMMUNICATION

- [ ] He will begin to recognize his own name.

SUGGESTIONS

- Around six months, your baby will give you clues that he is ready for food. Please consider three important points:

1. **Slowly introduce foods** and preferably introduce low allergy foods to minimize the risk of allergy and sensitivity. *Please see "Which Foods When" on our website.*

2. **Minimize your child's exposure to toxins.** Pollutants in our modern environment—for example pesticides, heavy metals, herbicides and fumigants—have been linked to abnormalities in behaviour, perception, cognition, and motor ability during early childhood, even when exposure is at so-called harmless levels. Therefore, try to provide your child with fresh air, organic food and a toxin-free environment. *Please see "Well Adjusted Babies" on our website.*

3. **Prioritize 'brain foods'.** Essential Fatty Acids (EFAs) are great brain foods and are found in cold-water oily fish, various oils such as macadamia, flaxseed and olive, some nuts and seeds, goat's milk products, blueberries and egg yolks. *Please refer to "Which Foods When" on our website.*

CRAWLING

When your baby crawls, both hemispheres of the brain must communicate and interchange information rapidly across the brain stem. What makes this incredible is that these same neurological routes are used later in life to perform more difficult tasks and in the capacity to multi-task.

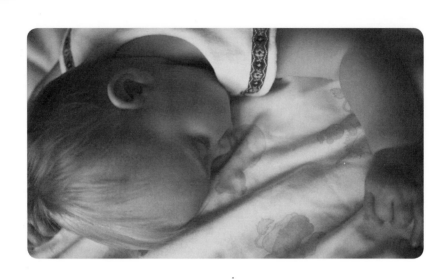

7 months

MOTOR

- [ ] Your baby may be able to sit up briefly and likes to sit alone.
- [ ] He likes to use his finger and thumb.
- [ ] He notices cause and effect.
- [ ] He can bite.
- [ ] He may be drinking from a cup.
- [ ] He starts combining skills, such as sitting and then lunging into a crawl, then back into a sitting position.

COMMUNICATION

- [ ] Your baby takes tremendous pleasure in loved ones and will remember them even when he hasn't seen them for a few days.
- [ ] He is wary of strangers.
- [ ] He may suffer separation anxiety if you go away.
- [ ] He will use his body to communicate with you, e.g. he will arch his back when you are holding him and he wants to get down.

SUGGESTIONS

- Be aware that between 7-24 months it is common for children to experience separation anxiety. Remain patient rather them pushing them to stay with strangers, as forcing them to stay in an environment can intensify the problem.

8 months

MOTOR

- [ ] Your baby likes to pivot on his stomach, throw things and bang toys together.
- [ ] Your baby should ideally be able to sit up unassisted.
- [ ] He will start to pull himself into a standing position.

COMMUNICATION

- [ ] Your baby may randomly use two syllable words, such as "dada".

SUGGESTIONS

- Interact with your baby and encourage him to imitate your arm movements

9 months

HEARING

- [ ] Your baby can associate voices and names with people, even on the phone.
- [ ] He will respond to music.

MOTOR

- [ ] He can sit up on his own, wriggle along on his stomach and will be close to crawling if he is not already.
- [ ] If he is strong enough, he may be able to use furniture to pull himself upright.
- [ ] He may be ready to take his first steps.
- [ ] He may be able to handle a baby spoon.
- [ ] He can drink from a cup.

COMMUNICATION

- [ ] Your baby can wave "bye-bye".
- [ ] He understands the concept of "no".

SUGGESTIONS

- Give him toys that squeak when he squeezes them (see "Safe Plastic Toys" on page 69).
- Play different types of music for him.

10 months

HEARING

- [ ] He will like to drop toys, watching and hearing them fall.

⚙ MOTOR

- [ ] Your baby likes to poke and prod with his fingers, and put smaller objects inside bigger objects.
- [ ] He may start to walk; babies usually start somewhere between the ages of 10-14 months.

COMMUNICATION

- [ ] He will imitate sounds.
- [ ] He may link his first recognizable word to a person, often "dada".

╫ SUGGESTIONS

- Use a soft ball to play with him.
- Explain activities to him, for example, while putting his socks on say, "Give me your foot and we'll put your sock on".

11-12 months

⚙ MOTOR

- [ ] Your baby is able to lower himself from a standing position.
- [ ] He can use crayons and imitates scribbling.
- [ ] He will throw objects intentionally.
- [ ] He can walk assisted by holding onto furniture or your hand.

COMMUNICATION

- [ ] He may say "ta" for thank you and will give you things if you ask.
- [ ] He will point to recognizable objects.
- [ ] His memory is developing well; he remembers what is behind closed doors, such as pots and pans in the cupboards.
- [ ] He often wants to join in conversations and loves to laugh.

╫ SUGGESTIONS

- Speak to him knowing he understands more than we realize.
- Teach him the names of friends and family.
- Show him how to place one block next to another or one block on top of another; teach him to count them.

12-18 mths

MOTOR

- [ ] The 'in-the-mouth' method of learning about the world usually disappears by this time.
- [ ] Your baby can turn two to three pages of a book at a time.
- [ ] His hand-eye coordination now becomes well established.
- [ ] Somewhere between 10-14 months he will begin to walk unassisted.
- [ ] Somewhere between 12-18 months he will begin to run – this will still be awkward.
- [ ] He is able to remove gloves, hats, socks and unzip jumpers.
- [ ] He is able to open cupboard doors.
- [ ] He can walk assisted up and down stairs.

COMMUNICATION

- [ ] Your baby has a vocabulary of two to three words.
- [ ] He plays near others but may not play with them.
- [ ] He will hug others, push, pull, snatch and grab, and defend himself.
- [ ] He talks to himself whilst playing.
- [ ] He probably won't ask for help.

PRIME YOUR BABY'S SENSES

Whenever possible, introduce new sensory experiences to your baby. Let them play with a range of objects which have different textures, temperatures or that make different sounds. Use the everyday world to excite their senses; have them run barefoot on the grass or sand, dip their fingers and toes in water, or play with rustling leaves.

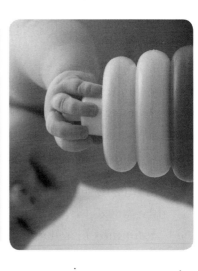

SUGGESTIONS

- Speak to him in full sentences.
- Encourage him with a range of objects and toys to do lots of self-play.
- Give him play-dough, clay etc – things he can mould.
- Give him toys he can pretend to feed, wash, clean their teeth and comb their hair.
- Give him ride-on toys to push himself along.

18 mths – 2 yrs

MOTOR

☐ By 18 months, your baby is becoming a toddler and he is ready to learn how to kick or throw a ball.

☐ He is keen to scribble with a crayon.

☐ He is able to turn the pages of a book one at a time.

COMMUNICATION

☐ He can say between 6 and 20 recognizable single words, but understands many more.

☐ Role play is now of great interest to little ones and your toddler will want to copy you by "cooking", "cleaning" and "doing repairs"!

☐ He will demonstrate frustration and impatience as he is eager for independence.

☐ Between 7-24 months it is common for children to experience separation anxiety.

SUGGESTIONS

• Speak to him in full sentences.

• Offer him a miniature broom, cloths to clean windows, mixing bowls, spoons and cups and small jugs of water and rice.

• Give him lots of colouring-in activities.

• Teach him different colours.

2yrs

MOTOR

- [ ] Your toddler now runs.
- [ ] He can negotiate stairs, placing two feet on each step.
- [ ] He can build a tower containing at least five blocks.
- [ ] He will attempt to copy you drawing a vertical line.
- [ ] He can push himself along on a tricycle.

COMMUNICATION

- [ ] He is able to identify and match some colors.
- [ ] He uses phrases made up of two or three words.
- [ ] He uses pronouns such as mine, me, you and I.
- [ ] He has a vocabulary of about 270 words.

BE ACTIVE

From an early age it is important to teach your child a range of physical activities so that they can learn to balance and coordinate their bodies. Activities like standing on one leg, hopping, skipping and walking along a beam or ledge (under supervision) are all helpful for balance, while spinning, swinging, ball games, clapping hands and cross crawling all provide wonderful brain feedback and can be introduced early.

SUGGESTIONS

- Continue to give him a dusting cloth or a brush and pan so he can mimic and help you with housework. Praise his efforts!
- Teach him to do stimulating activities like blowing bubbles or balloons, building with blocks or doing puzzles.
- Give him play-dough to pummel and pull apart. Ask him to make you specific things.
- Drape a blanket between two chairs to make a tent. Fill the tent with toys and let his imagination do the rest.
- Make sure he is getting ample sleep.
- Show him how to draw lines and a circle.
- Teach him his full name.
- Temper tantrums are common — be patient with him.

2–3yrs

MOTOR

- [ ] He can hold a crayon in his fist, and at 3 years he will start to hold the crayon with his fingers.
- [ ] He will attempt to copy a circle.
- [ ] He can hop on one leg and walk backwards.
- [ ] He can build a tower of about nine blocks.
- [ ] Between the ages of 2 to 4, he will learn to toilet train.

COMMUNICATION

- [ ] He refers to himself as "I".
- [ ] He can carry on a conversation.
- [ ] He is willing to wait his turn for something.

SUGGESTIONS

- Ask him to help put things away.
- Make sure your child is getting ample sleep.
- Encourage lots of imaginative play and dress-ups.
- Give him lots of colouring-in activities.
- Teach him short songs.
- Spend time each day reading to him.
- When he draws get him to tell you what he is drawing.
- Give him buckets of sand and water to play with.

3yrs

MOTOR

- [ ] Your toddler now climbs stairs using one foot on each step.
- [ ] He can balance on one leg.
- [ ] He begins to walk on tiptoes.
- [ ] He holds a crayon with his fingers.
- [ ] He can draw a circle and a cross.
- [ ] He catches a ball clumsily and forcefully kicks it.

COMMUNICATION

- [ ] He will know his first and last name.
- [ ] He expresses himself in four-word phrases.
- [ ] He may be shy or uncertain.
- [ ] He knows approximately 900 words.

SUGGESTIONS

- Encourage regular sharing of play things.
- Encourage him to dress himself under supervision.
- Give him lots of colouring-in activities.
- Make sure he is getting ample sleep.

3–4yrs

MOTOR

- [ ] Your child now walks up or down stairs with one foot on each step.
- [ ] He can hop on one foot.
- [ ] He is able to walk on heels.
- [ ] He can build a tower containing at least ten blocks.
- [ ] He can draw a man with a head, arms and legs.
- [ ] He begins to button or unbutton.
- [ ] He is able to take off his shoes.
- [ ] He is able to feed himself.

COMMUNICATION

- [ ] He is able to follow an instruction to place an item in, on top of or under another item.
- [ ] He knows his full name and age.
- [ ] He uses five-word phrases.
- [ ] He will have fewer temper tantrums as his communication builds.
- [ ] He will often be silly and do things wrong purposefully.

SUGGESTIONS

- Encourage him to feed himself.
- Encourage him to dress and undress himself.
- Ask him lots of questions and engage him in conversation.
- Make sure he is getting ample sleep.
- Offer him a safe painting environment.
- Teach him primary colours.
- Spend time each day reading to him.

4yrs

MOTOR

☐ Your child now walks down stairs with one foot on each step.

☐ He can hop on one foot.

☐ He can build a tower containing at least ten blocks.

☐ He can draw a man with a head, arms and legs.

☐ He should now be independent with the toilet.

COMMUNICATION

☐ His language should be fairly fluent.

☐ He listens attentively to others.

☐ He will ask lots of questions about the world around him.

☐ He can explain decisions that are made based on moral implications.

SUGGESTIONS

- Demonstrate how to use a pair of children's safety scissors.
- Allow time for him to dress himself.
- Explain the causes and effects of decisions.
- Give him opportunities to demonstrate his new level of responsibility.
- Let him plan an activity and execute it.
- Avoid over-stimulation by limiting his interactions with technology such as TV, gameboys, computers, etc.
- Make sure he is getting ample sleep.

TURN DOWN THE TV

Studies have found that 40% of households keep the television on 'in the background' and that this negatively affects children, decreasing both the quantity and quality of parent–child interactions. If you want to keep the television on, turn the volume down as this keeps the brain active.

4-5 years

MOTOR

- [ ] He runs and turns without losing balance.
- [ ] He can stand on tiptoes.
- [ ] He may stand on one leg for ten seconds.
- [ ] He can cut out pictures and paste them on paper.
- [ ] He can count to four or higher.
- [ ] He may be able to tie laces.

COMMUNICATION

- [ ] He can tell a simple story
- [ ] He knows the days of the week.
- [ ] He understands right and wrong.
- [ ] He will use lots of self-praise.

SUGGESTIONS

- Ask him questions like, "Which day comes after Tuesday?".
- Encourage outside play and ball skills.
- Encourage make-believe games.
- Encourage counting.
- Spend time each day reading to him.
- Show him how to write his name.
- Show him patterns and encourage him to create patterns.
- Make sure he has some lace-up shoes and show him how to tie them.
- Give him instructions that involve directions.
- Describe past, present and future events.

5-6 years

⚙ MOTOR

- ☐ He catches a ball and has lots of ball skills.
- ☐ He has good balance for climbing etc.
- ☐ His general co-ordination is improving.
- ☐ He can skip.
- ☐ He knows left from right.
- ☐ He will demonstrate an aptitude for right or left-handedness.
- ☐ He can draw a detailed house.

💬 COMMUNICATION

- ☐ He will use 6-7 word sentences.
- ☐ He is able to count to ten or more.
- ☐ He will start to recognize numbers 1-10.
- ☐ He develops the ability to share and take turns.
- ☐ His handwriting is more legible.
- ☐ Friends become more important in his life.

SUGGESTIONS

- Engage him with simple household chores.
- Play simple board games that have basic rules.
- Continue to teach him how to write his name.
- Get him to tell you when it is morning, afternoon and evening.
- Spend time each day reading to him.
- Give him games that require matching up pairs.
- Give him games that involve him making patterns and sequences independently.

6-7 years

MOTOR

- ☐ He can copy a triangle.
- ☐ He uses a pencil for printing his name.
- ☐ He will start writing more quickly.
- ☐ He will like stunts and gymnastics.

COMMUNICATION

- ☐ He can read one syllable words such as cat, dog etc.
- ☐ He begins to develop a basic vocabulary by figuring out words and choosing simple stories with illustrations.
- ☐ He asserts personal choice in decision-making and is aware of consequences of his choices.

SUGGESTIONS

- Give him games that require counters and grouping.
- Encourage inventive spelling and sounding out.
- Teach him simple time concepts.
- Have him cut out different shapes and tell you about them.
- Spend time each day reading to him.
- Encourage gymnastics, karate or other sporting activites.

Power to Parents

There is much effort and sacrifice required when raising vibrant, robust children but what each and every parent knows is that our children are worth such effort. With this section I would like to ask you, the reader, to collect your thoughts and ponder these few points...

3

Invest in 'you'

Have you ever noticed how you parent better when you are reading or listening to something inspiring, or when you are well rested and relaxed?

Obviously parenting isn't always 'peachy' but there will be activities in our day or week that nurture us as parents, times when we can invest in ourselves. This investment will make our parenting role less daunting and more blissful. We will feel refreshed and count our blessings, and be more inclined to notice what are children are doing 'right' and when they make an effort. We will also tune in to when they need us to sit down and cuddle them.

When we invest in ourselves we are happier, more resourceful, solution orientated and playful.

Here are some ideas of activities that 'invest in you':

- Going for a long run

- Taking 'nanna naps' on the couch

- Getting a massage

- Reading a novel

- Lying in the sun

- Listening to motivation CDs / audio books on your iPod

- A luxurious bath

- Filling your pantry with loads of fruit and vegetables

- Sleeping in late

- A swim in the ocean

- Less coffee, more water

- Buying some flowers

- Planning a few days' meals in advance or cooking a few meals at once

- Completing a task you have been putting off

- Going on holiday

- Seeing a funny movie

- Getting a chiropractic adjustment

- Visiting someone you love

- Planning a surprise for a family member

- Spending time with your beloved

- A walk in the rain

- See a Chinese medicine practitioner, homeopath, reflexologist or kinesiologist

- Making that dentist appointment

Question your intentions

Be aware of any deep-seated notions you may unconsciously carry regarding your child and your parenting. Some parents can fall prey to worrying that their child's personality is a direct reflection of themselves and their capacity to parent. They incessantly worry that other people judge them as a parent—with some people this may be true but ask yourself if these are the type of people you wish to associate with anyway?

Each individual child comes into this world with their own lessons to learn and their own oceans to sail—just like you and I. Life is too short to worry what other people think of you or your parenting.

It is important to ensure that we are not pushing our child to succeed for our own needs, such as our need to be validated and accepted.

Let your child be who they are

There is great value in seeing your child as a child and not as a trainee adult. Give them ample time to play and explore, to simply be a child. Make it safe for them to express their personalities, opinions and ideas. When we feel important and accepted as a child, this provides a springboard for true potential.

Refrain from comparing your child to other children or siblings. Pay attention to who your child is right now, not who you want them to be in the future.

Consider your past approach

Before embarking on change there is value in assessing your starting point and what has worked and not worked for you in the past. You may wish to rate your child's current physical or emotional health; is it poor, average or strong? And how would your lifestyle habits score; are they moving your family towards or away from greater health?

Consider what approaches you have taken before now and note their effectiveness or ineffectiveness.

Change your perspective

By this I mean stay open to new ideas and solutions. Past experiences may have been disheartening but trust that you will be guided to find the right contacts and resources that you need at each stage of your parenting.

Only with awareness

Celebrate the fact that you are reading books such as these and that you authentically want to help your child to be their best. Only with awareness and a learning attitude can we truly support our children. Parenting in this manner is not an easy ride—there are commitments with time, finances and energy—but it is a wonderful adventure nonetheless.

When you're a jerk, apologize and learn

Even proactive parents make mistakes—we are human after all. Rather than blaming any errors on our children, we can be mature enough to admit we behaved poorly, apologize and focus on creating new habits. It is when we repeat the same mistake over and over again that we really need to ask for help and to seek out new skills and parenting tools.

Value humour

Life can be way too serious, particularly if we are trying to balance life and work, the bank account and calendar events. When water is still through lack of movement it becomes stagnant, dark, dirty and smelly—much like our attitudes to life if we are not learning and growing. I don't strive for balance anymore; instead I appreciate that life ebbs and flows. Sometimes I work around the clock and at other times I play board games until my children say, "No more!" What I strive for is parenting the best way I can, all the while making my life purpose-filled.

It's easy to get serious when trying to juggle the daily grind. At the end of the day I like to ask myself if I had at least one special, fun moment with each of my boys—preferably more than one! If not, then perhaps I am suffering with a case of 'stinking thinking' or a 'bad attitude'. Life is fragile and precious, so spend it wisely and aim to laugh frequently.

> *"Laughter gives us distance.*
> *It allows us to step back from an*
> *event, deal with it and then move on."*
> —Bob Newhart

Look with your heart— not your eyes

I love the lyrics of this song from *Love Never Dies* where Katherine is telling her son not to judge the disfigured Phantom by his appearance. She sings, "Look with your heart but not with your eyes—close your eyes tight, the heart can't be fooled, the heart is too wise, forget what you think, ignore what you hear, look with your heart, it always sees clear".

The relevance here is that love is not always beautiful; sometimes in the heat of the moment our children may say hurtful things. In particular, parents with children who have ADHD may feel exhausted by their child's frustrated or aggressive behaviour. At times like these, it may help to "look with your heart, not your eyes". This is a practice of looking past the ugly words and deep into our child in order to feel what is happening for them.

At other times children may become distant or sullen and not say much at all. When asked, they may tell us, "Nothing's wrong." Again, look with your heart and trust your intuition.

Be a selective audience—consider what you are giving attention to

Sometimes we get hooked into our child's tantrum and we may even want to stomp after them and have the last word! Consider that a more effective approach is to withhold attention to poor behaviour and to dance with delight when they behave with wisdom and sensitivity. In this way they learn that self-mastery, communication skills and tuning into their environment brings them more acknowledgement then being a 'drama queen'.

Don't try to solve problems in the heat of the moment

If both you and your child are fighting, this is not the time to problem solve. Agree to revisit the issue when you are both calm. You can then aim to engage in 'active listening', whereby you each allow the other to speak and you make sure that you listen and acknowledge each other's points of view. You'll be amazed how solutions arise.

Don't run away with the ball

A girlfriend of mine uses a great analogy of 'running with the ball' to describe how parents often react to their children's problems; after listening briefly, we take the problem (or the ball) and run off with it by interfering, taking over and moving into 'management mode'.

An alternative is to stop and listen to our child with active listening skills. If our child is given time to express their feelings, they will typically do one of two things; they will either come up with a clear idea about how to move forward, or they will simply let the problem go.

Listening is an amazing tool which empowers children (and adults) to problem solve independently.

Maintain gratitude

Parenting is hard work but it is also extremely rewarding. Of all the blessings in my life, my children are my greatest. Each day I give thanks for who they are as individuals, what they teach me and who I am becoming through sharing my life with them and loving them.

When we focus on making sure our own heads and hearts are aligned, the role of parenting becomes far easier. We refrain from pushing our children forward and pushing against life itself.

Why Doesn't My Child Seem To Be Quite Right?

Why is my child not reaching their developmental milestones?

These are great questions...

U nfortunately, the answers are not simple as often there are a number of contributing factors that create a compounding effect for our children. The result is a child who is struggling to integrate their world, to learn, to express themselves, to interrelate and to be truly healthy.

In commencing this chapter we discussed how children develop at different stages. We have seen how a child's developmental pace can be influenced by their environment and the stressors or taxing agents of that environment. There is no need to panic if your child does not reach a developmental milestone at the same age as a friend, but it is important to follow your instincts and if you feel that your child is not as responsive as you think he should be or if he is less responsive then he has previously been, then certainly seek the advice of a professional.

Your child may be constantly immune-challenged, anxious or frustrated; whatever it may be, if you have a hunch that your little one is not 100% right, then source out practitioners and resources that can offer information and suggestions. Trust your heart and seek your own answers, as no one will go to the lengths that you will for your child.

Health is not simply a matter of 'feeling fine' or a lack of symptoms or illness. Health is "optimal physical, mental and social wellbeing", and this includes a body that is able to continually adapt to the stressors placed on it, recreating order and harmony. When our body is unable to adapt to the relentless physical, chemical and emotional stressors placed on it, our health is compromised.

The nervous system is an integral part of our body's health. When the body is out of balance due to stress, trauma or toxins, the function of the nervous system becomes impaired, resulting in a reduced flow of the life force.

Think of your brain as a computer and the nervous system as the hard drive of the computer. Your brain (computer) coordinates, via your nervous system (hard-drive), both organ and cell function. Nerve messages (in the hard-drive) can become impaired or blocked by spinal subluxations which occur when there are misalignments of one or more vertebrae. This results in altered joint motion and nerve irritation which lessens bio-communication, organ function and general health. The more severe and the longer the subluxation exists, the more profoundly 'dis-organized' the body becomes.

If you have a hunch that your little one is not 100% right, then source out practitioners and resources that can offer suggestions. Trust your heart and seek your own answers.

SPINAL CHART

Spinal Column Side View

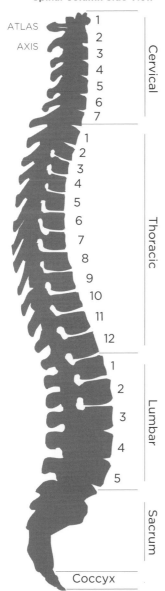

ATLAS
AXIS

Cervical — 1 2 3 4 5 6 7

Thoracic — 1 2 3 4 5 6 7 8 9 10 11 12

Lumbar — 1 2 3 4 5

Sacrum

Coccyx

Areas Supplied by Nerves

CERVICAL

1 Blood supply to the head, bones of the face, the scalp, the pituitary gland, the brain, the sympathetic nervous system, inner and middle ear
2 Eyes, auditory nerve, sinuses, tongue, forehead
3 Cheeks, outer ear, face bones
4 Nose, lips, teeth, palate, mouth, Eustachian tube, mucous membranes
5 Neck glands, vocal cords, pharynx
6 Muscles of the neck, shoulders, tonsils
7 Thyroid gland, shoulders down to the elbows

THORACIC

1 Oesophagus and trachea, forearms, hands, wrists and fingers
2 Heart and coronary arteries
3 Lungs, bronchial tubes, pleura, chest, breast, nipples
4 Gall bladder
5 Liver
6 Stomach
7 Pancreas, duodenum
8 Spleen, diaphragm
9 Adrenals or supra-renals
10 Kidneys
11 Kidneys, ureters
12 Small intestines, Fallopian tubes, lymph circulation

LUMBAR

1 Large intestines (colon)
2 Appendlx, abdomen, upper leg
3 Ovaries or testicles, uterus, sex organs, bladder, knee
4 Prostate gland, lower back muscles, sciatic nerve
5 Lower legs, ankle, feet, toes, arches

SACRUM

Hip bones, buttocks

COCCYX

Rectum, anus

Body out of Balance

The nervous system and body can become out of balance due to a number of contributing factors. For simplicity's sake I have divided these into Trauma, Stress and Toxins.

At other times a body may be out of balance due to a chromosomal disorder or severe illness—this is always an extremely challenging scenario. These children have individual needs and yet some of the information conveyed here may also assist them in better integrating their world.

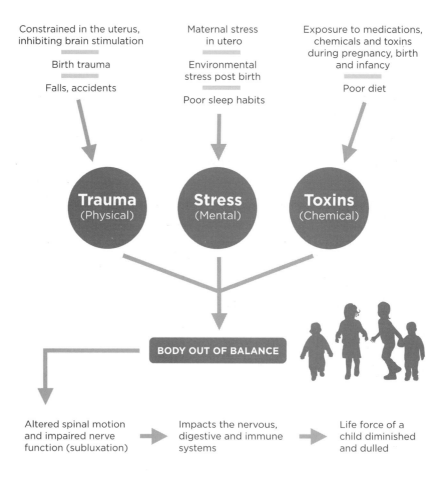

Body out of Balance: Trauma (Physical)

A lack of movement in the womb and birth trauma

A LACK OF MOVEMENT IN THE WOMB

Literature shows that vertebral subluxations or irritation of the spine and the nervous system can be caused during pregnancy due to a mother's pelvic distortion (misalignment of the bones of the pelvis) or the position of the baby within the uterus.

How does this happen?

Previous accidents (e.g. motor vehicle, cycling), falls (e.g. off horses, down stairs) or poor postures may have allowed the joints in the pelvis to move into awkard positions. When the joints of a mother's pelvis do not sit correctly, the layers of muscles, ligaments and other connective tissue that surround a growing baby are pulled out of shape, creating an uneven tightening of the uterus and limiting how a baby moves within the pelvis. As a baby grows bigger their movement may become significantly inhibited as the tissues become more restrictive.

Research tells us that movement within the womb is vitally important for developing babies; i.e. by moving about during gestation, babies stimulate the development of their brain and nervous system. Research suggests that a lack of mobility may be one contributing factor for developmental delay.[1]

Clinical studies on General Movements (GMs) of foetuses in the womb have been found to be extremely beneficial in predicting a developing baby's neural activity and function; i.e. brain function. Studies in 2011 published in *The Journal of Early Human*

Development[2] found that **abnormal GMs from conception up to 3-4 months of age were associated not only with a high risk for cerebral palsy, genetic disorders, minor neurological deficits and behavioural problems but also with lower intelligence.**

Being restricted in the pelvis, particularly for some time, may impact a baby's long-term development. Ideal spinal alignment—that which ensures adequate room for developing babies to move and grow within the pelvis—is one reason that chiropractors adjust pregnant women. This supports the health and wellbeing for mother and child.

BIRTH TRAUMA

Spine and nerve distress can arise from restricted or abnormal positioning in the uterus and also from the journey through the birth canal or during the delivery process itself.

According to Gutmann,[3] a researcher who examined the effects of the birth process, "the trauma from the birth process remains an under-publicized and therefore significantly under-treated problem." There are many factors that can cause birth trauma, including false labour, a long or very short labour, failure of the mother's cervix to dilate, the use of drugs to increase contraction intensity, the use of vacuum extraction or forceps, caesarean section delivery, cord around the baby's neck and foetal distress. Unfortunately, many couples are unaware that using pain relief during labour often leads to a more complicated birth, potentially involving forceps or ventouse.

While nerve irritation can be caused with assisted deliveries, even straightforward vaginal births can create vertebral subluxations if the baby's head and neck are not tucked under fully to allow for even distribution of the forces associated with labour contractions. Over 1500 babies were studied[4] periodically across an eight year period by Viola Frymann, an American osteopathic doctor. All babies were examined within the first five days of birth; in fact, many were checked within the first 24 hours of birth. This study revealed that approximately:

- 10% of the newborn babies had perfect, freely mobile skulls or cranial mechanisms.

- 10% had severe trauma to the head, evident even to untrained observers.

- The remaining 80% all had some strain patterns in the skull or cranial mechanism.

This fascinating study revealed that at least 90% of the babies involved had suffered birth trauma and had associated strain through the neck and cranial areas. This is why chiropractors recommend all babies have their spine and nervous system checked post-birth to help ensure spine and nerve dysfunction does not impact their capacity to breastfeed and digest milk, sleep or integrate their world.

OTHER PHYSICAL TRAUMAS

A newborn's spine is extremely vulnerable and poor handling by adults or older siblings may be another cause for vertebral subluxation. In fact, subluxations occur throughout life, particularly as we learn how to walk, ride and climb. Other physical causes for subluxations include accidents during contact sports, activities such as skate-boarding and surfing, sustained postures with electronic equipment and poor posture in general.

One study examined a group of apparently healthy children and found that 15.8% had cervical subluxations (neck problems) and 40% had pelvic subluxations.[5]

Body out of Balance: Stress (Mental)

Maternal stress in-utero

Science is now beginning to realise that a foetus is actually a human being and that the womb is not just an incubator, it is a dynamic living environment greatly influenced by the physical, chemical and emotional stress its parents experience. The study of epigenetics looks at how the pre-conceptive, pre-natal and post-natal environments influence the health of our children long-term. We discuss the impact which in-utero maternal stress has on a developing brain in a later section, *Potential Contributing Factors for Autism*.

Environmental stress post-birth

An environment can be considered hostile when a child feels their safety or the safety of either parent is threatened, or when the environment itself feels stressful or uneasy. These feelings in turn create physiological responses from the body which can result in anxiety, personality issues or health complaints. Epigenetics and other areas of research show us that emotional stress affects both children and adults at a cellular level, creating change that can be detrimental.[6]

Poor sleep habits

Emotional stress for babies and children (even adults!) can be caused by poor sleeping habits.

If a baby or child does not wake up easily and with energy each morning, this could indicate they are not getting enough quality sleep, which in turn will affect their personality development, their learning and their health in general. As a mother of four, I know

that children may at times resist going to bed; however, if this becomes an ongoing issue then they will certainly become over-tired, which will have a ripple effect on the whole family.

If your child consistently wakes up tired or is slow in the morning, then try getting them to bed an hour earlier for a period of time and watch how this can transform grumpy or emotional behaviour. Over the years I have learnt that a set routine for dinner and bedtime makes life easier for everyone. This means aiming to feed children early—well before they are tired. Plan an ideal time for bed and give yourself plenty of time for baths and the reading of evening books, etc. Some nights you will be able to have luxurious, long baths and other nights you will need to be drill-sergeant.

SLEEP HABITS FOR NEWBORNS

As a new parent I had no idea about sleep routines for babies. New parents are often shocked that newborns initially sleep and feed around the clock. The average newborn will sleep 16 out of 24 hours but all babies are different and you may find your baby sleeps up to 19 hours a day or as little as eight. You needn't worry about how many hours they sleep—you have either a wakeful baby or a sleepy one.

In those first few weeks, newborns will wake, feed and then fall asleep again, only to wake 2–3 hours later for another feed. As your baby grows he will want bigger feeds, become more active in between sleeps and sleep for longer periods during the night. By six months, most babies will have developed a fairly regular pattern. The key to establishing a good sleep routine for your baby is to help him to differentiate between night and day, and to teach him that the longest periods of sleep should be at night. Be aware that babies quickly learn to settle into the same routine every night.

The following table may provide parents with a guide to sleeping patterns of newborns. Remember this is only a guide; all babies vary and nine hours at night certainly does not infer "nine hours of solid sleep without waking during this time for a feed".

HOW MUCH SLEEP DOES YOUR CHILD NEED PER DAY?

AGE	TOTAL	NAP TIME	NIGHT SLEEP
Newborn	17hrs	8hrs	9hrs
2 months	15-16hrs	5-6hrs	10hrs
4 months	15-16 hrs	4-5 hrs	11 hrs
6-9 months	14-15 hrs	3-4 hrs	11 hrs
12 months	13-14 hrs	2-3 hrs	11 hrs
Up to 3 years	12-13 hrs	1-2 hrs	11 hrs
3-6 years	11-12 hrs	(every 2-3 days)	11-12 hrs
7-12 years	11 hrs	-	11 hrs
12-15 years	10-11 hrs	-	10-11 hrs
16-18 years	9-10 hrs	-	9-10 hrs

If you have concerns that your newborn is not sleeping enough, please consider the following:

- If your newborn is breastfed, are there items in your diet that could be stimulating the infant (e.g. coffee, tea or chocolate) or aggravating (allergens, alcohol, fizzy drinks)? *Please refer to www.welladjusted.me for the eBook on Breastfeeding.*

- Seek advice on baby cues and on wrapping and swaddling newborns. The DVD "Happiest Baby on the Block" is a wonderful resource for new parents. Doulas and midwives are also incredibly adept at helping with these problems.

- Consider having your newborn assessed for nerve dysfunction associated with their birth by a chiropractor.

WHAT ABOUT SLEEP ROUTINES FOR YOUNG BABIES?

Some women take great pride in telling other mothers that they've gotten their child to sleep through the night or that their child only feeds when it is the 'right' time. Contrary to popular belief, parenting is not a competition. Some mothers feel like failures if their child wakes through the night or still demands feeds at six, twelve or 24 months. There is no right or wrong. What is important is choosing your own style of parenting, knowing that you are nurturing your child in a manner that supports your beliefs and core values.

Some parents do train their child to 'sleep through' from a very early age but if it is indeed 'training', then what is the cost? Does this traineeship cause your baby unnecessary emotional stress? Be sure that you are not trying to discipline your baby merely to impress others with your parental capabilities. If order and routine are essential for you to maintain peace in your life, then it is important that you honour your needs; however, if they are not essential, then just be yourself. Relax and follow your heart and let the patterns unfold.

Personally, I am very fond of quality sleep—that is, the far, distant memory I have of quality sleep! As our small children grow, I trust that this simple pleasure will re-enter our lives. For now, we try to create a balance between teaching our children about the importance of sleep and also being available to calm and soothe. The time you have with your baby during their first twelve months is so precious and you would do well to try not to make it too regimented. There are many resources available for parents that discuss wonderful sleep-promoting techniques. Pinky McKay's books, *Parenting by Heart* and *100 Ways to Calm the Crying*, offer a beautiful guide to gentle nurturing with confidence.

OLDER CHILDREN AND SLEEP

With social, school and family activities, bedtimes can gradually become later and later for older children; however, sleep requirements remain just as vital for teenagers as when they are younger. It turns out that many teenagers may actually need more sleep than in their previous years. It is a good idea to limit the number of late nights that children have in a week. Although social pressures may conspire against our best intentions, we need to place great value on the proper amount and quality of sleep. Children cannot learn or play sports well when their bodies are chronically tired.

A WORD FOR TIRED PARENTS

Catch 'nanna naps' whenever you can—fatigue is a terrible thing. Lack of sleep can affect every aspect of your life. My number one tip for parents with small children is to prioritize sleep any way you can.

When we are tired our thoughts seem to spiral down. It is imperative that when fatigue hits we remind ourselves that our thoughts create our reality and in turn, our reality creates our world. At these times we can also draw on our family and friends for support and read good books to help inspire us. The ability we have as human beings to be our very own alchemists and turn negative energies into awareness, honesty and courage never ceases to amaze me.

"We do have a zeal for laughter in most situations, give or take a coffee."
—Dr Simon Floreani

Body out of Balance: Toxins (Chemicals)

Exposure to medications, chemicals and toxins during pregnancy, birth and infancy

Unborn babies and breastfed children are exposed to chemicals through maternal diet and the toxins that a mother inhales or that pass through her skin from the environment. Accumulation of these toxins can directly impact a mother and child's nerve and immune systems.

"But aren't unborn babies protected by the placental barrier?" you may ask.

IS THE PLACENTA A PROTECTIVE BARRIER?

Not long ago scientists thought that the placenta shielded an unborn baby from most toxins a mother consumed and most of our mothers believed this wholeheartedly. What we now know is that the umbilical cord carries not only the building blocks of life but also a steady stream of industrial chemicals, pollutants and pesticides that cross the placenta just as readily as residues from cigarettes and alcohol.[7]

WHAT DOES THE PLACENTA DO?

The placenta is an organ attached to the lining of the uterus during pregnancy. It is linked to the baby by the umbilical cord, which passes oxygen and food to the foetus. Waste products from the baby, such as carbon dioxide, pass back along the umbilical cord to the placenta and then into the mother's bloodstream for her body to eliminate.

The placenta also produces hormones that help your baby to grow and develop. It may also provide some protection against bacteria and infection; however, it does not protect your baby against viruses such as German measles.

Towards the end of pregnancy the umbilical cord pulses with the equivalent of at least 300 litres of blood each day, passing antibodies from the mother to baby and giving the baby immunity for about three months after birth.

WHY THE PLACENTA IS NOT THE BARRIER WE ONCE THOUGHT

While the placenta may offer some protection from infection it does not provide a barrier against the passage of alcohol, nicotine and other drugs as we once thought—these can cause damage to our unborn babies.

Clinical studies tell us that up to 60% of what we put onto our skin makes its way into our bloodstream.[8] Direct absorption through the skin means that substances bypass the body's major filtering organs such as the kidneys and the liver, which would normally assist with toxin removal. Researchers can now demonstrate that once these chemicals enter the bloodstream they can be transferred to the foetus.

In a study[9] spearheaded by the Environmental Working Group (EWG) in collaboration with the Commonwealth, researchers at two major laboratories found an average of 200 industrial chemicals and pollutants in umbilical cord blood from ten babies born in August and September of 2004 in US hospitals. Tests revealed a total of 287 chemicals in the group. The umbilical cord blood of these ten children harboured pesticides, consumer product ingredients and wastes from burning coal, gasoline and garbage. Among them were eight perfluorochemicals used as stain and oil repellants in fast-food packaging, clothes and textiles (including the Teflon chemical PFOA), dozens of widely used brominated flame retardants and their toxic by-products, and numerous pesticides.

Of the 287 chemicals detected in this umbilical cord blood, we know that:

- 180 cause cancer in humans or animals;

- 217 are toxic to the brain and nervous system;

- 208 cause birth defects or abnormal development in animal tests.

The dangers of pre- or post-natal exposure to this complex mixture of carcinogens, developmental toxins and neurotoxins have never been studied.

It would seem that the human 'body burden'—the pollution that permeates the cells of our body—also deeply influences babies in the womb. **With this in mind I would urge all couples planning to conceive and those who are currently pregnant to take great care with all items they consume, the quality of the foods they eat and the quality of their water and other beverages, and to avoid alcohol and other drugs where possible.**

EVERYDAY ROUTES OF TOXIN EXPOSURE

The following diagram outlines how these chemicals pass to the developing baby or the breastfed infant. Please consider the chemicals in your self-care products and other 'nasties' in your home and workplace.

EVERY DAY ROUTES OF TOXIN EXPOSURE

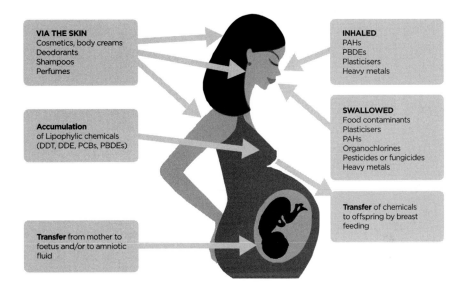

VIA THE SKIN
Cosmetics, body creams
Deodorants
Shampoos
Perfumes

INHALED
PAHs
PBDEs
Plasticisers
Heavy metals

Accumulation
of Lipophylic chemicals
(DDT, DDE, PCBs, PBDEs)

SWALLOWED
Food contaminants
Plasticisers
PAHs
Organochlorines
Pesticides or fungicides
Heavy metals

Transfer of chemicals
to offspring by breast
feeding

Transfer from mother to
foetus and/or to amniotic
fluid

Pesticides, colourings, additives and hormones in foods are all toxic to the body, as are most over-the-counter and prescriptive drugs. Research now shows that chemicals which influence our hormonal system may in fact create changes to the cells of the body that pass from one generation to another.[10] More than ever before there is great need to be aware of environmental toxins, and pregnant mothers in particular need to be aware of their exposure to chemicals in their day-to-day living that will pass to a developing baby.

Some breastfeeding mothers may look at this graphic of *Everyday Routes of Toxin Exposure* and have concerns regarding this siphoning-off process of chemicals to their child when breastfeeding. Research tells us though that the benefits of physically and emotionally nurturing our babies through breastfeeding still outweigh any risk of exposure to maternal toxins.

OTHER CHEMICALS IN A CHILD'S HOME

In Chapter 1, *Minimize Your Child's Exposure to Toxins*, we discussed some environmental chemicals to be mindful of that find their way into our foods and our homes. On the facing page are chemicals to watch out for in personal care products.

"Man shapes himself through decisions that shape his environment."
— Rene Dubos

NASTIES IN PERSONAL CARE PRODUCTS

SHAMPOOS & CONDITIONERS

Look for products free of: Sodium lauryl sulfate, or SLS (makes products foam and create suds), propylene glycol, artificial fragrance, alkylphenol ethoxylates, ammonium laureth sulfate, laureth sulfate, artificial colours disguised as coal tar (FD, FDC or FD & C colour), sodium oleth sulfate, sodium (PCA/NAPCA).

Alkylphenol ethoxylates, widely used in shampoo, has also been found to reduce sperm count and to mimic oestrogen in the body.

Most artificial fragrances used in shampoo, hairspray, deodorant, nail polish, etc, may contain **phthalates.** Fragrances are also linked to liver cancer in lab animals and asthma in children.

TOOTHPASTES

Look for brands free of: SLS, laureth sulfate, fluoride, polysorbate 80, artificial colours disguised as coal tar (FD, FDC or FD & C colour). Also avoid tooth whiteners and brighteners in general.

DEODORANTS

Look for products free of: Propylene glycol and aluminium. Select roll-on or pump spray varieties rather than aerosols containing propellants.

LAUNDRY AND HOUSEHOLD CLEANING PRODUCTS

Look for brands free of: formaldehyde, phosphates, chlorine, chloroform, tri-ethanolamine (TEA) and diethanolamine (DEA).

For more information please see Chapters 14 and 25 of Well Adjusted Babies, or download the eBooks on our website: www.welladjusted.me.

POOR DIETARY HABITS

The old saying of "we are what we eat" is very true, however, we are also "how well we digest and absorb our food". There are many people who eat extremely 'well' and yet they are not as healthy and vibrant as they could be due to poor digestion and absorption—leading to an array of health problems including food sensitivities, fatigue and migraines—and elimination problems which can result in constipation, diarrhoea and more sinister diseases such as cancer.

An adult's digestive health experience is most certainly related to the digestive strength established and fostered during childhood. Inappropriate food introduction during childhood can compromise digestive strength for life.

Infants are born with immature digestive systems that are not able to easily break down and assimilate or absorb foods. The enzymes of an infant's digestive system are neither plentiful nor efficient. The digestive system is also extremely porous (thinly walled), hence the importance of the correct introduction of solid foods. *This principal is so important that I have dedicated an entire eBook to discussing the introduction of solids and wholesome eating—please see "Which Foods When" on our website (www.welladjusted.me).*

Sadly, millions of children suffer with eczema, asthma and allergies, while research indicates that proper nutrition is fundamental to developing a strong immune system. Poor sleep patterns, irrational behaviour and learning disabilities have all been linked to diet. The advice that often accompanies the popular 'food pyramid' culture to "just feed your child a balanced diet" is simply not enough to raise strong, healthy children.

Children require specific food preparations until their digestive capacity has had sufficient time to mature. A child's future digestive capacity can in fact be weakened by early exposure to poor food choices and common dietary allergens.

Digestive weakness can persist, increasing the likelihood of chronic childhood and adult illnesses, moving the body further and further out of balance.

The digestive system houses the largest part of a child's immune system; in fact, it is estimated that approximately 60% of our immune cells reside in our colon (bowel). Unfortunately, toxins and dietary allergens can fundamentally affect and overload our digestive capacity and impact our immune system.

The top eight allergens responsible for 90% of food-related allergic reactions are: milk, wheat, soy, eggs, peanuts, tree nuts, fish and shellfish. Ironically most of these foods are the standard foods parents are recommended to introduce when their child starts eating solids. However, with the careful introduction of certain foods at particular ages, we can potentially minimize food sensitivities and allergies. If an older child already exhibits an allergy, periods of desensitization can prove highly beneficial.

Proper introduction of solids based on the latest research and wholesome nutritional principals is imperative. Often the advice we receive, however, is based on the promotional gimmicks of the food industry, perhaps using celebrity athletes who have invested interests in certain product lines. As parents we need to be well read and discerning.

Improving our awareness about food helps us to also identify food additives and preservatives. These substances (or mixtures of substances) present in food as a result of any aspect of production, storage or packaging. Studies show that more than 100 of these chemicals have the potential to cause cancer, genetic defects and abnormalities in the developing foetus. There is much to learn if we desire to protect the digestive health of our children. Of the 47 colourings approved for use in foods, thirteen are azo dyes or coal tar dyes; these synthetic compounds are known to cause allergic reactions in some people, while coal tar dyes can cause cancer in animals.[11] *(If you would like further information about digestive health please visit our website at www.welladjusted.me)*

A diet devoid of proper nutrients and poor hydration (lack of water) allows toxins to accumulate in the body. The longer the toxins remain and accumulate, the weaker the core energy of the body becomes.

PROBIOTICS: A CRITICAL STEP IN DIGESTIVE HEALTH

Our modern lifestyle taxes our digestive strength every day—hence the profound need for high quality probiotics. More and more research is showing just how essential to health probiotics are for all ages, including newborns and infants.

When we consider the impact of chemical exposure during pregnancy as discussed in the section *"Exposure to Medications, Chemicals and Toxins During Pregnancy, Birth and Infancy"*, we can appreciate how a child's digestive system is depleted by the toxic load well before they are even breathing independently or eating!!!

Newborn babies benefit from probiotics given daily via breast milk, on the nipple itself or mixed into formulas. Offering probiotics well before the introduction of solid food provides a critical period of repair and support for an infant's digestive system. Probiotics are vital to strengthening digestive health before introducing any solid foods let alone the common allergenic foods which are typically recommended at six months of age.

There are a number of studies showing the benefit of 'good' bacteria for an array of childhood health issues such as colic, eczema, asthma and gastrointestinal symptoms associated with autism. Acidophilus is often promoted via the media as the only bacterium needed; however, it is just one strain of bacteria that inhabits a specific part of our bowel. There are in fact about 500 other beneficial strains of bacteria that play a vital role in helping to keep the gut clean and healthy.

It is important to source a high quality probiotic formula ideal for everyday support of gut health and digestive function in children. Ask your health practitioner for a product which contains therapeutic probiotic strains that support digestive health, boost the immune system and can help with an array of health issues such as dermatitis, eczema, food allergies, candida and respiratory tract infections, for example.

SO WHAT KILLS OFF THE HEALTHY BACTERIA FOUND IN OUR GUT?

Poor dietary habits, antibiotics and environmental toxins destroy important flora or good bacteria of the bowel. There are many environmental toxins that tax the delicate digestive balance, including:[12]

- Chlorine found in water

- Fluoride found in water and other products

- Pesticides and herbicides

- Air pollution

- Household and personal care products

- Drugs (including antibiotics and the oral contraceptive pill) and alcohol

- Stress

WHEN TO START PROBIOTICS AND HOW OFTEN?

In most circumstances, parents should be able to start their newborns on a dairy-free probiotic almost straight away. Mothers who breastfeed can take probiotics themselves and rub probiotics onto their nipples before a feed, while bottle-fed newborns can receive probiotics by mixing these beneficial powders into a bottle of formula after hot water has been added.

For older babies, parents can provide infants with probiotics by mixing them into their foods. Ideally newborns and infants can have one serve of probiotics a day.

WHEN TO START SOLID FOODS?

For parents of young babies, knowing what to feed their infant can be very confusing. We need to understand which foods should be given and when, based upon the availability of digestive enzymes. Many people have hypersensitivities or allergies which, literature suggests, may be due to premature exposure to certain food groups.[13]

I have discussed digestive principles in more detail in Well Adjusted Babies (2nd Edition). For more information, please see our website, www.welladjusted.me.

At around six months of age (for some it is later) your baby will be eager to embark on the journey of culinary delights. Some parents may be advised that offering solid foods prior to this time will help their infant sleep but let me stress that premature food introduction will not help a baby to be more settled or sleep for longer periods and may increase the risk of developing food sensitivities.

It is important to wait until your child is ready for this next stage. Some of the usual signs that your baby is ready for solid foods are:

- Your baby has the ability to sit up well.

- Your baby seems hungrier than usual between breast or formula feeds and does not seem as content or settled after the feeds. They may also seem to drain your breast quickly or be frustrated during a feed.

- Your baby seems interested in food. Initially they will be fascinated by the 'motions' of a parent eating, and over the following few weeks they will start to reach for your fork, pull at your hand and verbalize their interest.

- Your baby starts moving their tongue back and forth in their mouth, rather than up and down in a sucking motion (this means they are ready to move food from their lips to their throat).

It may still be too early for solids if they spit the food out or simply drool, keeping the food in their mouth without swallowing. Wait a couple more weeks and then try again. If your baby does spit out these initial foods, this does not mean that they do not like this particular food item or that you should try another food; it may simply means that your child is not ready for solids.

Research suggests that solely breastfeeding for the first year will only delay the onset of food allergies and not prevent them altogether. After six months, breast milk will start to become depleted in iron, zinc and vitamin C.[14] Therefore, slow introduction of quality nutrition, with special attention to Essential Fatty Acids (EFAs), is more effective in preventing allergies than delaying solid foods.[15]

For more information, please see Chapter 22, Which Foods When and Chapter 23, Ten Best Nutrition Tips for the New Millennium of Well Adjusted Babies—these chapters can be individually downloaded from our website www.welladjusted.me.

Allergies move a body out of balance

COMMON SYMPTOMS OF ALLERGIC REACTIONS

Allergies and sensitivities can be diverse. When a child has chronic allergies and sensitivities this is a sign that the body is struggling to recreate body order.

Most of us, when we think of food allergies, reflect on the dangerous reactions to classic foods such as milk, wheat, soy, eggs, peanuts, tree nuts, fish or shellfish. These are known as Classic Food Allergies or Type 1 allergies. They evoke an immediate response from the immune system and they usually incite a quick itchy rash or a breathing or gastric reaction, and sometimes may even be fatal.

More commonplace are Type 2 allergies, known as food intolerances or sensitivities, such as those caused by wheat or dairy, where reactions can be difficult to identify and isolate. Food intolerances build up over time and can come and go with age. They are usually created by foods eaten repeatedly.

Many of the chemicals currently found in our foods also create intolerances known as Food Additive Reactions. Other foods create allergic reactions by building up in the body until they induce a reaction. These allergic reactions are dose-related.

SIGNS OF ALLERGY

- Flushing

- Rashes

- Itching

- Vomiting

- Swelling of lips, tongue and throat
- Difficulty breathing, asthma

THE ALLERGIC FACE

- Runny congested nose
- Dark rings under the eyes
- Red ears
- Eczema

Your infant may show all of these signs or just a few.

SIGNS OF FOOD INTOLERANCE

- Congestion with coughing, sniffling and runny nose
- Eczema
- Rash around the mouth
- Sever nappy rash
- Asthma
- Glue ear
- Headaches or migraines
- Aching muscles and joints
- Infantile insomnia
- Poor appetite
- Vomiting
- Stomach aches, colic (in babies)
- Persistent diarrhoea
- Behavioural disorders, including hyperactivity

'Poo tips' for adults and children

Have you ever wondered how often you should poo?
Or if your poo was healthy?

Okay, after we get passed the awkwardness of this topic, most of us would admit we are a little intrigued.

How often we use our bowels and what our poo looks like tells us a lot about our general health and wellbeing.

Without realizing it, many of us put 'clag-like' products into our bodies 3-5 times a day, such as white and multigrain breads (the grains and seeds are simply added to the 'glue' which doesn't help), biscuits, cakes and other white flour products.

If we then forget to eat fruit and vegetables, drink water or exercise, we may find we only poo once every few days and that we have bloated tummies.

Unfortunately, if we don't tune in to our bowel health and teach our children to do the same, over a period of time our whole body, including our brain function, will start to be affected.

WHAT MAKES POO HEALTHY?

So now that we've started to tackle this topic we need to really engage—which means you are going to have to look at your poo and teach your child to look at their poo—yep, that's right, you will need to actually look at the shape and the colour.

A HEALTHY POO:

- Tells us when it is ready to come out

- Slips out easily

- Is well formed (poo should look like a brown banana with a point at one end or an 'S' shape)

- Is well hydrated (poo that looks like little balls wadded together has been in the colon too long)

WHAT IS NOT A GOOD SIGN?

- Having no urge

- It hurts

- It takes a long time

- The poo is always very loose and fast

- The poo looks like little balls or pieces

- There's blood or mucus

TIPS TO FOSTER BOWEL HEALTH

If you are a parent it is important to make poo habits and digestive health a part of natural family conversation. The easier it is to talk about poo, the easier it is to correct poor habits.

Two to three good bowel movements a day is considered optimal digestive health; in fact, many children poo after each meal.

Drink plenty of water—on average at least 30 ml for every kilogram (or 1 ounce for every pound). Here are some examples:

*   For a 40 kg child, multiply by 30 ml: they should be drinking at least 1200 ml (1.2 litres) of water.

*   For an 80 kg person, multiply by 30 ml: they should be drinking at least 2400mls (2.4 litres) of water.

Cut out too much Coffee (dries out the bowel), **Refined sugars** (breeds bad bacteria), **Antibiotics** (strips away good bacteria) and **Processed foods**—*or you could just remember to cut out CRAP, but that would be cheeky!*

Eat stacks of fruit and vegetables—strive for 10-15 pieces a day. One 'piece' is considered roughly the size or length of your hand, such as one apple or one carrot.

Remember to chew not just swallow food. Slow down and be mindful of what you're eating. Chewing food helps kick-start the digestive process.

Prioritize eating foods that look as nature intended them, i.e. foods that look the same as they did when they were extracted from the ground or the garden. Remember, there are no white bread plants!!

Eat whole-grain products, preferably gluten-free, such as kamut, spelt and quinoa; these help flush fat and cholesterol out of your system. Don't mistake whole-wheat products for whole-grain.

Perform some form of **sweaty exercise** five days a week. When we are stagnant our bowels become stagnant.

De-stress and slow life down. When we are stressed we are typically not moving with the flow of life. Let your life and bowels flow.

Check your 'bowel transit time'. When the digestive system is working well, bowel transit time ranges from 12 to 24 hours.

To easily test transit time, simply eat a brightly coloured food such as beetroot (at least one or two whole beets), take a mental note of the time it is eaten and then check each motion to see when a dark red poo emerges.

Alternative foods you could trial include corn and sesame seeds. Corn is a grain, not a vegetable, and is extremely hard for the body to digest and assimilate.

Because it passes through the digestive tract mostly undigested, it is a particularly useful food for this transit test.

7 REASONS WE MAY BECOME CONSTIPATED

We can't poo when:

1.   We haven't drunk enough water.

2.   We haven't eaten enough fibre or bulk (fruits and vegetables).

3. Our spine is not aligned; vertebral subluxations affect nerve messages between the brain and bowel (chiropractic assists the nervous system re-create body order).

4. Our foods are not well combined (an imbalance in consistency or flavouring).

5. We haven't exercised enough.

6. We are emotionally tense.

7. We keep ourselves too busy, rushing them from one activity to another.

AWKWARD... BUT IMPORTANT

So while poo may be an awkward topic, it makes sense to check in with our body and identify how our bowels are coping with our lifestyle stressors. If we have children then it is wise to make bowel health a very normal part of family discussion.

Clearly we are not just talking about bathroom habits—we are appreciating that a lack of health affects so many aspects of our lives. When our bowels work well they extract the vitamins and minerals we need to thrive and they remove the toxins we gather from modern living.

Good bowel health gives us energy and vitality and allows us to fight off infections and illness. Healthy bowels create healthy bodies and when our body is working well, so too is our mind and we are better able to integrate and connect with the world around us.

Early signs of a body out of balance

As parents it is important we observe our children to see that they are integrating their world around them. The developmental charts shown previously in this book are designed to help parents assess how well their child is moving through the milestones relevant to their age and to encourage parents to engage with their child at different ages. Following is a list of signs that may indicate your child is not thriving as well as they can, which can be used in conjunction with the developmental charts discussed. *This list is not conclusive and imbalance can be indicated in other ways.* If you have any concerns, please seek the advice of a chiropractor or registered health professional.

NEWBORN TO 18 MONTHS OLD

HEAD AND BODY:

- Head tilted to one side, ears and eyes uneven

- Uneven head shape, flat or pointed areas

- Body looks uneven; for example, shoulders are not level

- Baby lies on an angle

- Obvious muscle tension (baby doesn't look relaxed) or a lack of muscle tone ('floppy' baby)

SKIN COLOUR:

- Pale skin

- Skin bags under the eyes, either pale or dark yellow/brown

- Excessive cradle cap, rashes or eczema

MOVEMENT AND SPEECH:

- Doesn't like 'tummy time'; cries or is uncomfortable when placed on tummy

- Hardly ever cries

- Inability to lift the head and neck

- Not a lot of movement; typically stays in one position

- Delays with crawling and walking

- Is not making many baby noises or mimicing words

FEEDING AND DIGESTION:

- Cries or fusses during feeding

- Arches back

- Seems agitated or uncomfortable

- Colicky, is frustrated

- Spits up a lot

- Doesn't burp easily

- Has gas

- Prefers to feed on only one side

- Lacks interest or strength when feeding

- Latches on, then pulls off

- Poor suck and swallow

- Consistently falls asleep when feeding

- Drooling; constant or profuse

- Bowels do not move after each feed

- Constipated for one or more days

SLEEP:

- Listless

- Needs to be woken up for feeding

- Never sleeps deeply, only naps

OTHER GENERAL HEALTH SIGNS:

- Slow recovery from minor illnesses

- Recurring illness with increasing symptoms

- Not reaching other developmental milestones discussed in the *Developmental Charts*

18 MONTHS PLUS

HEAD SHAPE AND FACIAL EXPRESSION:

- Shows severe head misalignment

- Dull look with few expressions

- Mouth open, corners not tight

- Not very alert or awake

MOVEMENT, VISION, HEARING AND SPEECH:

- Rapid and uncontrollable movement

- Lacks balance and coordination

- Arms are too weak to raise up to head height

- Hands never relax or open

- Stiff and hard to hold

- Seems agitated or fretful

- Breathing not deep or rhythmic

- No eye contact; appears to look straight ahead, through you, not at you

- Eyes uneven, vision not synchronized

- Head movement only; eyes not moving to corners

- Over sensitive to environmental noises

- Almost oblivious to environmental noises

- Hardly ever cries, seems weak

- Always fussy and cries uncontrollably

- Only mimics sounds with unusual speech patterns

- May not mimic sounds or speak

SKIN COLOUR:

- Pale skin

- Skin bags under the eyes, either pale or dark yellow/brown

- Excessive cradle cap, rashes or eczema

SLEEP:

- Listless

- Needs to be woken up for feeding

- Never sleeps deeply, only naps

- Sleeps all the time

DIGESTION AND EXCRETION:

- Bloated tummy or extended bowel

- Foul-smelling poo (should be a sweet smell)

- Bowels do not move after each feed

- Constipated for one or more days

- Poo is too loose or too hard (like little balls)

- The balance of liquid intake to rate of urination output is inconsistent

OTHER GENERAL HEALTH SIGNS:

- Bed-wetting

- Weak, tires quickly

- Not willing to participate in favourite activities and has trouble keeping up with peers

- Slow recovery from minor illnesses

- Recurring illness with increasing symptoms

- Not affectionate or happy

- Not curious, lacks enthusiasm for life

- Often frustrated

- Withdrawn

- Defiant and angry

- Hyperactive

- Cannot relax at night, trouble sleeping

- Sluggish and fatigued upon waking

- Poor dietary choices

- Not reaching other developmental milestones discussed in the *Developmental Charts*

Getting in Balance

In the previous chapters of this book we have addressed a number of themes that help us:

- protect our child's health;

- restore our child's health, moving them towards a state of balance;

- enhance our child's health.

When a child has decreased nerve function due to subluxation for any of the reasons discussed in the previous chapters via trauma, stress or toxins or a combination of these, their body moves further away from a state of balance and their life force is diminished. With time these modern lifestyle stressors cause body weakness resulting in a lack of function, coordination and synchronization of the body.

DR JEN, WHAT WOULD YOU DO IF THIS WAS YOUR CHILD?

I am often asked this question and I will visit it again in Chapter 5 with relation to ADHD and autism. For the purpose of this section let's us discuss what I would do for a child that, for example, has chronic colds and flus, a loose bowel, limited speech and erratic sleep patterns? I will outline here in point form my approach...

STEP 1

1. I would look through the *Early Signs of a Body out of Balance* and note any area you feel your child might not be 100% well.
2. Consider how frequently they get colds and flus.
3. Observe your child for signs of food allergy (as outlined in this chapter).
4. Assess if your child is getting enough sleep (as outlined in this chapter).
5. Assess their diet for intake of processed foods containing additives, colourings and preservatives (please see Resource Section for useful websites).
6. Assess how much water they are drinking.
7. Consider how much fruit and vegetables they eat in their day.
8. Assess how often they use their bowels—please refer to the section *'Poo Tips' For Adults and Children*.
9. Calculate how many prescription medications they have had in their lifetime.
10. Recall what accidents and falls they have endured.
11. Recall your pregnancy and the birth, and consider any possible discomfort or trauma during this time.
12. Rate your child's overall health (0 = extremely poor, 10 = fabulous).
13. Ask friends and family for a recommended chiropractor and other holistic health practitioners who are confident working with children.

STEP 2

1. See a wellness oriented chiropractor.
2. Source practitioner-grade probiotics and EFA supplements—take daily.
3. Find a recommended multi-mineral drink or powder.
4. Buy a water filter.
5. Eat brain foods and good fats every day.
6. Commit your child to daily cross-crawling exercise.
7. Stock the fridge with an abundance of fresh fruit and vegetables, preferably organic.
8. Do an audit of your pantry and throw out as many processed foods as you can.
9. Learn how to identify chemicals in the ingredients lists of food items (see Resource Section for websites such as "Additive Alert).
10. Do an audit of your personal care products, such as shampoos, bubble baths, etc (see Resource Section for websites such as "Skin Deep Database").
11. Explore new bed-time rituals to facilitate better sleep.
12. Engage in some form of physical exercise each day.
13. Book yourself on a parenting course or read some parenting books—there's always room for improvement!
14. Cut out allergy foods and try an elimination diet—if you need some advice, see a naturopath.
15. Create laughter in the home with plenty of tickles and commit to expressing more affection.
16. Limit television and electronic time.
17. Refer to More 'Feel Good' Moments, Less 'Out-of-Sorts' Moments in Chapter 1 and learn how neurochemicals influence our child.
18. Spend time with your child each day, engaging and connecting with them, free of agendas.
19. Investigate acupuncture and homeopathy.
20. Invest in 'you'.

A HEALTHY LIFESTYLE FOR TODAY'S FAMILIES

The following graphic of *A Healthy Lifestyle for Today's Families* demonstrates all of the areas we need to focus on to raise vibrant, robust children.

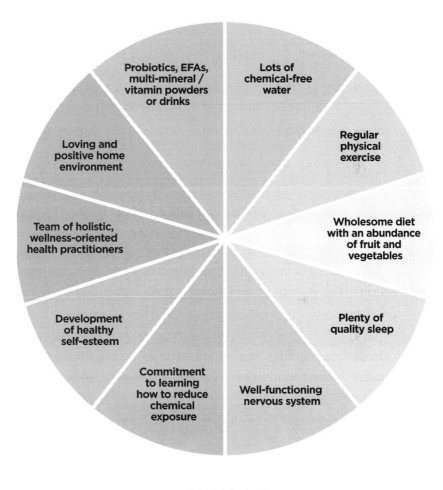

© Well Adjusted™

www.WellAdjusted.me

Chiropractic care

In Chapters 1 and 4 of this book we looked at the number of ways a child's body can move away from a state of health and order towards a state of poor function and disorder. These chapters clearly outline today's lifestyle factors which impact our child's health and specifically the function of the nervous system. Whether we have a large spine or a tiny little spine, if we have nerve distress then our magnificent bodies cannot operate smoothly.

The nervous system is the master controller of our body and if its communication channels become fuzzy, distorted or damaged then we experience all sorts of communication errors. We have seen that for babies and children this ineffective communication may play out as colic or irritability, an inability to suckle and breastfeed, poor sleep, developmental delays, digestion issues, asthma, behavioural problems, low energy, inability to concentrate, headaches, etc—the list is endless.

While chiropractic may be able to help with a number of health issues, our focus is not on treating or curing ailments; our focus is to ensure the nervous system has every opportunity to work efficiently and effectively.

For example, imagine your nervous system is like the lighting system in your home. If the lights start to dim, you might not be able to cook dinner very well, you may start banging into furniture, you may trip and hurt yourself, you may feel frightened, etc. Exactly how the dim lights influence you will vary but the issue is still the same—there is a communication problem between the wiring and the intended outcome which needs detecting and fixing.

In the same way, chiropractors spend years studying the nervous system to be able to detect and correct these 'communication errors' in the body.

Chiropractic is the largest, most regulated, drug-free, primary healthcare profession in the Western world.[16] While chiropractic care is by no means a cure-all, by improving the level of function of your spine and nervous system, the body is able to recalibrate and recreate balance so that overall body function improves. Chiropractors will work with parents and other practitioners when needed to address other lifestyle factors that may be depleting your child's life force, such as poor diet or exposure to toxins.

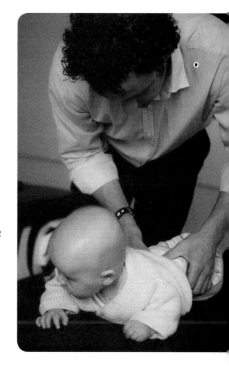

As their spine and nerve function improves, children will respond in different ways. Their bowels may work more regularly and their immunity may be strengthened. Some children may become calmer, less hyperactive and more focused, while others may become less rigid, demanding, angry or defiant.

More and more chiropractors are working with pregnant couples to help facilitate straightforward births. They are checking newborn babies to ease birth trauma and checking children of all ages to help keep their bodies in balance. Chiropractic adjustments for newborns and children differ significantly from those performed on adults. Infant adjustments are very gentle, and typically a baby will be soothed by these techniques.

If you are concerned that your child has a more serious health challenge such as ADHD or autism, please see related chapters and know that chiropractors happily work with medical practitioners and other allied health practitioners to help ensure the best outcomes for your child are achieved.

Understanding Signs of ADHD, Autism, Asperger's Syndrome and Companion Disorders

You may have worked through the previous chapters and now be wondering if your child has a more profound health challenge such as ADHD or autism. Please know that if this is the case, there are many resources available and many wonderful, caring practitioners who can support and guide you and your child.

When a child is disconnected from their world it is indeed a lonely and sad experience for them, and having to observe this as a parent can be extremely painful. Parents may also have to manage erratic, demanding or distressing behaviour and it can be hard for families who have not experienced ADHD, autism and Asperger's Syndrome to comprehend the enormity of this type of parent-child relationship.

So who am I to write about how parents can approach this health challenge?

As a chiropractor of a large, multidisciplinary centre, I have worked with many families afflicted by ADHD, autism, Asperger's and a host of other health conditions, and I have worked collaboratively on these issues with various allied health practitioners. In caring for such families, I am privy to their needs, their questions and their

stories of prior experience. Sometimes these parents have had a negative experience with doctors or practitioners, resulting in them feeling overwhelmed or frustrated. For example, some practitioners may suggest that certain activities or treatment plans are futile for children suffering from these conditions.

When faced with any advice, I like to remind parents to always trust their heart and to ask themselves, "Do I feel that it is the best thing for me to do right now?" If not, seek an alternative opinion or revisit the advice at a later time.

When choosing a practitioner, ask, "Is this practitioner willing to work with me and with other health practitioners for the benefit of my child?" It is important that you make decisions about your own life and your child's life rather then feeling pushed into a form of care that does not align with your vision.

Aside from my professional experience, I have some personal experience to draw upon when working with challenging children or those who have brain injuries and chromosomal or genetic disorders. When I was almost seven months pregnant with our third son, we discovered he had a fatal heart condition which was later identified as a spasmodic developmental disorder known as 'isomerism'. Alarm bells were then raised when we had four weeks of uterine growth in only two weeks.

Even though specialists told us to expect the worst, our most natural inclination was to stay hopeful. We believed it would not serve our baby or our family to give up prematurely. We decided to do all that we could physically, emotionally and spiritually to 'parent' our baby at this time. I spent hours meditating and connecting with our baby, time which enabled me to replace feelings of anxiety with a sense of peace and reflection on what life was helping me to learn. I had numerous chiropractic adjustments, ingested Chinese herbs and had several healings and energy balances with different practitioners. We spoke to a variety of people who had shared similar experiences and we received so much love and support from an array of people, it was quite overwhelming.

Towards the end of that week I felt intuitively that our baby had died and so, when the subsequent ultrasound revealed this outcome, I felt strangely calm. We made arrangements to return to the hospital that evening and induce our labour.

After discussions with our midwife, I decided not to have painkillers so that I would be 100% emotionally present during the birth. I believed that experiencing the physical pain of the birth would allow for more natural grieving, and such grieving would allow for greater healing.

Well, the intensity of the labour certainly did encourage us to grieve heavily; the labour was quick, acutely painful and completely overwhelming. We named our baby Abraham (Abe) and spent the next few hours holding him and blessing him. Even after experiencing such an extremely sad labour, the hardest part for both Simon and me was what came next—leaving our baby behind at the hospital.

I remember holding Abe and stroking him again and again, whispering tender goodbyes. Every part of my body ached. With each step I took from his side I felt as if someone was taking my heart and leaving in its place the deepest of wounds.

My body ached for my baby for weeks and months to the point where I was physically ill. I worked hard on acknowledging my fears and my anger and pleaded with my Lord to help me stay centred. It was a grueling time.

To this day my longing for Abe still grips me, makes my knees give way and my heart sink.

While it may sound odd, I know that should Abe have lived, no matter what condition he may have entered the world, I would have wanted to parent him and to be his life source and mother. When you hold your child who has died in your arms, you are forever changed. You develop such a deep gratitude for all children in varied shaped and sizes.

So who am I to discuss children with ADHD, autism and the like? Well, I am a parent and practitioner who genuinely wants to help these little people—to stir the magic within them, to teach them to hold their heads high and show the world their full character and brilliance.

Attention Deficit Hyperactivity Disorder (ADHD)

ADHD is known to have two main components: impulsive, poorly self-monitored behaviour and problems with learning, attention and short-term memory. It is characterized by an early onset of persistent and impairing levels of inattention, disorganization and hyperactivity. ADHD is now estimated to affect between 5-10% of school-aged children and is the most commonly diagnosed behavioural disorder of childhood.[1]

It's important to recognize that a child with ADHD is not being difficult intentionally. Nor is ADHD the result of poor parenting. ADHD is certainly multi-factorial. Diagnosing ADHD can be difficult as there is no single test but early identification can substantially alter the child's educational and social development. Before diagnosis it is advisable to rule out straightforward causes of ADHD symptoms, such as nutritional deficiencies, allergies or food intolerances and sleep disorders such as sleep apnoea.

Symptoms commonly seen in ADHD sufferers:

- Struggles to stay focused
- Doesn't appear to listen to instructions
- Inattentive
- Easily distracted and disorganized
- Needs constant attention
- Disruptive
- Impulsive; acts before thinking
- May be violent towards other children when frustrated
- Accident-prone
- Hyperactive; needs constant activity
- Talks excessively

Unfortunately these behaviours are so persistent in children with ADHD that they interfere with daily life and the child's ability to learn.

HEROES AND HIGH ACHIEVERS WITH ADHD

As we discussed in in the Introduction of this book, some of the world's greatest heroes are individuals who have defied constraints or labels that society had once placed on them and they have made a remarkable impact on our world. Each person listed is recorded as having ADHD or the equivalent of ADHD for that era of time.

Thomas Edison	Bill Gates
Albert Einstein	Ernest Hemingway
Leonardo da Vinci	Alfred Hitchcock
Salvador Dali	Jim Carey
Emily Dickinson	Christopher Columbus
Jamie Oliver	John D. Rockefeller
Justin Timberlake	Nelson Rockefeller
Beethoven	Sir Richard Branson
President George Bush (Senior and Junior)	Michael Phelps
	Eleanor Roosevelt
Andrew Carnegie	Pablo Picasso
Will Smith	Dustin Hoffman
Henry Ford	Elvis
Benjamin Franklin	John Lennon
Galileo	Thomas Jefferson

In offering this list of well known people with ADHD I am not suggesting that every ADHD child can be moulded into Bill Gates nor that that should be our intention. I offer this list as a reminder for parents that our goal is to help free the potential and magnificence in our children, and that when we feel like the future is bleak, to remember to focus on the little steps and to always believe in our children's capacity to thrive.

COMPANION DISORDERS

There are several disorders that may occur with ADHD, including the following: Conduct Disorder, Oppositional Defiant Disorder, Anxiety Disorder and Obsessive Compulsive Disorder.

Proactive approaches to ADHD and companion disorders

NUTRITION

A well-balanced diet rich in micronutrients is an essential starting point for managing a child with behavioural problems. Food additives have been used in processed food in increasing quantities since the 1960s, and since this time we have also seen a sharp increase in children's behavioural disorders.[2] We are surrounded by food items filled with additives, colourings and preservatives—indeed, it is estimated that the average American eats an alarming 14 pounds (6.36 kilograms) of additives each year![3]

There is increasing evidence that many children with behavioural problems are sensitive to one or more food components that can negatively affect their behaviour. Food additives, refined sugars, food allergies and essential fatty acid (EFA) deficiencies have all been linked to ADHD.[4]

Irritability, restlessness, inattention and sleep disturbances (rather than hyperactivity) were the effects of food additives, as noted by researchers in a Melbourne study[5] of children aged 2–6. Children aged 7–14 were irritable, aimlessly active, lacking in self-control, whiny and unhappy. In light of this information, it is interesting to note that the latest childhood behavioural condition, known as Oppositional Defiant Disorder, lists irritability as the core behavioural effect.[6]

Studies from the UK have shown that 79% of hyperactive children are allergic to the yellow colouring Tartrazine (102, C.I. 19140, or FD & C Yellow 5), a coal tar dye. Potential health effects include aggressive behaviour, headache, insomnia, hay fever, asthma and hyperactivity.[7] Tartrazine is banned from foods in Norway and its use is heavily restricted in Austria, Sweden and Germany. Sadly, this colouring is approved and frequently used in both the United States and Australia. It is found in soft drinks, confectionery, cereals (such as cornflakes and muesli), yoghurt, snack foods (such as corn chips), cordials and oral medications.[8]

In a report on the safety of these common food dyes, Executive Director Michael Jacobson from the Center for Science in the Public Interest (CSPI) stated, "These synthetic chemicals do absolutely nothing to improve the nutritional quality or safety of foods, but trigger behaviour problems in children and, possibly, cancer in anybody. The Food and Drug Administration should ban dyes, which would force industry to colour foods with real food ingredients, not toxic petrochemicals." [9]

The micro-nutritional aspects of child behavioural problems are often neglected. For example, iron deficiency, which is the most common of all the nutritional deficiencies, can lead to poor concentration and behavioural problems,[10] while magnesium deficiency can cause irritability and decreased attention span; this deficiency has been found in 95% of children with ADHD.[11] It is recommended, in order to reduce magnesium loss, children should not be given soft drinks. Omega-3 fatty acid deficiency may also lead to ADHD[12] and lower levels of zinc are commonly seen in children with ADHD compared with normal children.[13]

Candida albicans is a bacterial imbalance leading to a yeast infection. Candida is commonly seen in children with autism, ADD and ADHD, and some studies suggest this may be due to increased antibiotic use in these children (please see *Autistic Spectrum Disorders – Contributing Factors*) Candida has many systemic effects on the body and tackling this yeast overgrowth is essential for strengthening physical, mental and emotional wellbeing. *Please see Chapter 4 for further information regarding the benefits of probiotics for candida.*

A healthy diet that includes supplementation may be an effective means of managing ADHD. One study of hyperactive children compared the use of the drug Ritalin versus a diet supplemented with different vitamins, minerals, phytonutrients, amino acids, essential fatty acids, phospholipids and probiotics. Amazingly, in both groups there were similar outcomes, suggesting that dietary supplementation may be as effective as Ritalin in treating ADHD.[14]

Be sure to investigate any micronutritional deficiencies your child may have and please see later in this chapter; *Dr Jen what would you do if this was your child?*

ENVIRONMENTAL CHEMICALS

We have discussed the harmful impact environmental chemicals can have on young children in Chapter 1, *Minimize Your Child's Exposure to Toxins,* and I ask you to review this section. Here we looked at studies that link phthlates with ADHD symptoms and Bisphenol A with hyperactivity.

EMPOWERING BEHAVIOURAL STRATEGIES

I have a deep respect for parents of children with ADHD, mostly because of their deep commitment to these beautiful human beings. I can appreciate that at times children with ADHD do not seem beautiful—in fact, sometimes these little ones can be mean and hurtful. But as we discussed in *Power To Parents*, it pays to remember to "look with your heart, not your eyes".

ADHD children need simplicity with boundaries. Consistent guidelines for behaviour in the home and at school can assist the child to monitor and accept responsibility for their behaviour. Rules need to be clear and simple, with only one or two instructions given at a time, and it is important to recognize and praise these children when they behave appropriately. (For more ideas, please see *More 'Feel Good' Moments, Less 'Out-of-Sorts' Moments.*)

Laughter is the shortest distance between two people.
—Victor Borge

There are several different approaches to working with ADHD and these disorders, including Cognitive Behaviour Therapy, in which a doctor, psychologist or other health professional talks with the child about their symptoms and alternative ways to cope with them. Biofeedback has also been found to be helpful in allowing children to control the speed of their brain waves. One study found that doing so led to a 25% decrease in ADHD symptoms.[15]

In some cases, medication may be helpful but this is something a psychiatrist can advise you about. Before resorting to medication I would suggest working with a number of holistic health practitioners including chiropractors, naturopaths or Chinese

medicine practitioners. The knowledge and skill of these practitioners can help to recreate body balance and is always a safer first step than medication.

TUNE THE NERVOUS SYSTEM WITH CHIROPRACTIC

A study of 24 children with behavioural problems and learning disabilities compared three different treatments: chiropractic adjustments and cross-crawl exercises; chiropractic adjustments alone; and medication. It was found that chiropractic adjustments were more effective than medication across thirteen different measured areas and with no side effects.[16]

Chiropractic does not focus on relieving ADHD symptoms but focuses instead on improving neural function. While not every child will respond as favourably to chiropractic care as the study suggests, when the nervous system communicates more clearly the mind and body move back towards a more balanced state. Many case studies also confirm the relationship between chiropractic adjustments and decreased hyperactivity.[17]

MEDICATION

Ritalin has been the drug treatment of choice for ADHD. Researchers now agree on some of the known side effects, which include: stunting of growth, depression, chronic headaches, nervousness, skin rashes, high blood pressure, pulse changes and the development of Tourette's Syndrome.[18] According to *Medical Economics*, the chronic use of Ritalin has also produced psychosis and the main complication of Ritalin withdrawal is suicide.[19]

Dr Daryl Efron, researcher and paediatrician at the Royal Children's Hospital, Melbourne, Australia, says that Australian doctors are following United States trends by now prescribing an increasing range of mood-altering and behaviour-controlling drugs to children. "These medications are even being given to children younger than three, while little is known about long-term effects, particularly the mixing of medications. This is a cause for concern and we need guidelines on their use." [20]

Before rushing to medicate your child for a behavioural disorder, please consider that there may be other safer and equally effective forms of care. There are also many holistic practitioners who have success working with behavioural disorders. The individual skills of one practitioner alone may be limited, so practitioners often work together, combining their expertise and knowledge.

Please also refer to "Dr Jen, what would you do if this was your child?" later in this chapter.

Autism Spectrum Disorders

Autism is a label or diagnosis that creates fear for most parents. Autism is part of a spectrum of neurodevelopmental disorders characterized by repetitive behaviours and impaired language and social interaction. Its prevalence has dramatically surged in recent decades. In Australia, autism now affects one in 160 children aged 6–12 years and approximately 1 in every 150 children in the USA.[21] It occurs in all racial, ethnic and social groups and is four times more likely to strike boys than girls.[22]

Autism is a complex neurological disorder that affects a person's ability to communicate and relate to the world around them. It is usually apparent by the age of three, and as with ADHD, effective early intervention can significantly improve a child's outcomes.

The Australian Autism Handbook, by O'Reilly and Smith,[23] describes early signs that can be cause for concern:

- Lack of babbling or pointing by 12 months

- No shared interest in objects or activities with another person

- No single words by 16 months

- No two-word phrases by 24 months

- Flat facial expression and vocal tone

- Repetition of heard words

- Lack of eye contact

On their own, these signs may not indicate autism but they should be sufficient to warrant an assessment.

AUTISM SYMPTOMS

Autism affects children in varied ways. Some children will have obvious autistic behaviours, such as flapping their hands, no speech at all and be seemingly unaware of those around them. Others will have subtle symptoms, such as severely limited interests and social problems, so may not be diagnosed until they are older.

The three core symptoms associated with autism include:

- Flawed communication

- Impaired social interaction

- Repetitive behaviour

Parents are usually the first to notice unusual behaviour in their child or their child's failure to reach age-appropriate developmental milestones. Some parents describe a child that seemed different from birth, while others say that their child was developmentally normally and then lost certain skills.

There are several different diagnoses which come under the Autism Spectrum Disorders (ASD) umbrella: Autistic Disorder (classical autism); Asperger's Syndrome; Rett's Disorder; and Childhood Disintegrative Disorder. All of these conditions share symptoms of limited social skills, communication difficulties and restricted and repetitive interests and behaviours. Sometimes the child may also have an intellectual impairment. Many children with autism are also sensitive to sensory stimuli, such as touch or sound.

Autism is detected by several screening checklists, which rely on parent interviews and direct observations of the child. After the initial assessment, a child's progress can be monitored and, if necessary, early intervention can commence. Most diagnoses are made when the child is 2-3 years old. A child with Asperger's Syndrome or high functioning autism may not be diagnosed until they're much older because they have a normal IQ and develop language normally. Their symptoms are more subtle but these children still experience enormous difficulties with social interactions as they are unable to read social cues and body language.

FOUR FACTORS TO WATCH OUT FOR

While the biology of autism remains elusive, many genetic and environmental factors have been identified and investigated as potentially triggering the disorder. Two pioneers in autism management, Sidney M. Baker and Richard A. Kunin, identified toxic environmental changes that have occurred in developed societies between 1950 and 2000 that may be associated with the autism upsurge. These have included:[24]

• Increased antibiotic use

• Mercury exposure by injection in infancy

• Increased combined live viral vaccines and numbers of vaccinations

• Increased soil depletion leading to vitamin/mineral deficits

• Decreased omega-3 fatty acids in the diet

• Greater exposure to xenobiotic toxins (chemicals capable of mimicking the body's natural biochemicals)

Whilst no individual factor has been definitively shown to cause autism, pollutants in our modern environment such as pesticides, heavy metals, herbicides and fumigants have been linked to abnormalities in behaviour, perception, cognition and motor ability during early childhood, even at low and apparently harmless levels.[25]

1. OXYTOCIN

There have been many studies that have looked at how oxytocin influences autism. It is reported that autistic children have deficits in oxytocin-processing peptides and that when oxytocin plasma levels are at a normal level (i.e. for those not within the autistic spectrum), individuals were found to demonstrate mastery over appropriate social skills.[26]

Evidence suggests that abnormalities in the neural pathways for either oxytocin or vasopressin (both hormones which play a role in governing human behaviour and bonding) could account for many aspects of autism including the repetitive behaviours, early onset, learning deficits, alterations in neural development and a predominance in boys. Human studies provide further support for the theory that autism may be linked to oxytocin dysfunction. Two related studies in adults, in 2003 and 2007, found that oxytocin decreased repetitive behaviours and improved interpretation of emotions.[27] More recently, intranasal administration of oxytocin was found to increase emotion recognition in children as young as twelve who were diagnosed with autism spectrum disorders.[28]

A 2004 review[29] proposed that excess oxytocin, a drug frequently used to induce and augment labour, could contribute to the development of autism. The author stated that there are two barriers commonly thought to prevent oxytocin from reaching the infant's brain during labour: the maternal placenta barrier and the blood brain barrier of the infant. However, birthing factors may make it possible for oxytocin to permeate the blood brain barrier, desensitize oxytocin receptors and lead to changes in neurology and behaviour.

2. PRENATAL STRESS

Prenatal exposure to stressful events has also been associated with increased risk of autism.[30]

Epigenetics is an area of science that is gaining greater and greater credibility. It examines the interplay between genetics and the environment, and within this scope there are many studies that look at the relationship between pregnancy, gestational stress and post-natal development.

To understand epigenetics, it helps to think of normal body function as a carefully orchestrated symphony of chemical messages working together in rhythm to express health. Exposure to dietary and environmental toxins or stressors interferes with developmental messages and the music may then begin to lose its harmony.

A retrospective study demonstrated that mothers of autistic children reported significantly more family discord during their pregnancies.[31] Another study found that 188 mothers of autistic children reported significantly more stressful life events (such as a job loss or the death of a husband) during their pregnancies than the 202 mothers of normally developing children.[32] Several other studies described by Kinney et al[33] have demonstrated that prenatal exposure to natural disasters significantly increased the risk for a variety of behavioural disorders in infants.

3. EXPOSURE TO HEAVY METALS — MERCURY, LEAD AND ZINC

Mercury is a known neurotoxin, a brain poison that has been linked with many forms of brain damage. A 2006 study[34] looked at baby teeth as a measure of cumulative exposure to toxic metals during foetal development and early infancy, specifically comparing the level of mercury, lead and zinc in the baby teeth of autistic children with those of normally developing children. It was found that children with autism had significantly (2.1 fold) higher levels of mercury but similar levels of lead and zinc.

4. ANTIBIOTICS AND GUT PROBLEMS

These same children discussed in the study above also had a significantly higher usage of oral antibiotics during their first 12 months of life. The authors described how antibiotic use is known to completely prevent the excretion of mercury in rats due to changes in normal gut flora. They hypothesized that the high use of antibiotics in autistic children may in turn reduce their ability to excrete mercury. Further noted were the high numbers of gastrointestinal issues in autistic children, potentially explained by the normal gut flora changes caused by frequent antibiotic use.

A study by Dr Joan Fallon[35] similarly demonstrates the prevalent use of antibiotics in autistic children and makes note of the association between the introduction of the antibiotic Clavulanate Amoxicillin in the 1980s and the dramatic rise in autism cases at the same time. In her study an exceptionally high number of ear infection episodes were found, with each child having received a mean number of 12.04 courses of antibiotics—a sum total of 2480 courses of antibiotics given to the 206 children in the study.

Fallon proposed that the potentially high levels of urea ammonia yielded by clavulanate in children warrants further investigation as a potential autism cause. Fallon also questions whether autism is a brain disorder or a gut disorder,[36] given the high number of autistic children with gut problems. Augmentin, an antibiotic known to cause gut irritation, may contribute to inadequate digestion of foods and damage to the small intestine and pancreas resulting in allergens and pathogens passing through the gut lining. Fallon suggests that improper digestion of fats and proteins may consequently harm the rapidly growing brain of children, potentially contributing to the multi-factorial nature of autism.

When weighing up the risks and perceived benefits associated with taking antibiotics, some parents may feel that the effectiveness of these drugs outweighs potential dangers. However, if you have ever wondered whether antibiotics are as effective as we have been led to believe and would like additional information on safe alternatives, please visit our website at www.welladjusted.me.

There is also great benefit in utilizing high quality probiotics to re-strengthen the gut. *For more information on this, please see the Probiotics section in Chapter 3 of this book.*

GETTING SUPPORT

Parents who have recently been told that their child has autism may feel hesitant to look for potential causes of autism and this is understandable. However, I recently shared this book with a mother of a newly diagnosed autistic child; she found she was able to use the book's content to help clarify her concerns. Rather than getting fixed on the 'autistic' label, we looked at the whole health picture for her child so we could prioritize lifestyle factors and determine how best to move forward.

It is important to consider the factors that may have contributed to a child entering the autistic spectrum. Contemplating these factors doesn't change the current reality of the situation but it can help when selecting management and lifestyle approaches. If you have concerns about your child's behavioural development, your first stop should be your GP, for a referral to a developmental paediatrician.

For parents whose children have been diagnosed as autistic, organizations such as *MINND* (catering for Metabolic, Immunologic, Neurologic, Digestive, Developmental conditions), *Defeat Autism Now!* (DAN!) and *Autism360* may offer some support.

Parents need to get as much information as possible about ASD and its interventions. *The Australian Autism Handbook* is helpful, as is the website *www.autismawareness.com.au*. While there is no known cure as such, there is a considerable and growing body of evidence that shows significant improvement in the functioning of autistic children who receive early treatment.

The intervention program should ideally be intensive—between 20 and 40 hours per week. Finding and accessing a good intensive intervention program can be overwhelming and expensive, but there are also some limited, non-intensive programs available. With good quality early intervention, children who have been diagnosed with autism can achieve considerable gains that will make a significant difference to their lives and those of their families.

As a chiropractor, experience has taught me that when families work with these organizations and with a team of holistic health practitioners, they can:

- Learn new skills to connect and communicate in a way that meets the child's needs;

- Learn how to rebuild the gut strength of a child challenged with autism;

- Gain specific dietary advice and move away from a self-limiting diet;

- Learn how to progressively detoxify (homeopathy works very well here);

- Have chiropractic adjustments to free up their nervous system.

This combination of factors certainly helps to create more significant health outcomes for an autistic child than simply tackling this challenge with only one approach.

Please also refer to "Dr Jen, what would you do if this was your child?" later in this chapter.

Asperger's Syndrome

Asperger's Syndrome (AS) is a mental developmental disorder at the higher end of the autism spectrum. AS sufferers do not have significant delays in early language development, learning or self-help skills (in fact, many AS people are highly intelligent), and the disorder is often detected later than autism because speech usually develops at the expected age. Asperger's may be genetically linked.

Symptoms of AS can include:

- Difficulty in forming friendships, understanding rules of social behaviour and reading the body language of others.

- Advanced language skills when compared to peers but difficulty with communication, particularly listening.

- A narrow field of interests; the person may be able to talk extensively on a topic of interest but have difficulty with daily tasks, understanding jokes or sarcasm. They will understand statements in a literal sense.

- Lack of coordination with activities such as handwriting, ball skills, riding a bike or sports.

- Repetitive patterns of behaviour and activities.

- Heightened sensitivity to noise and touch.

- Flapping their arms in anger and possibly hitting others.

Asperger's Syndrome was first described by Hans Asperger in 1944 as a mild form of "high-functioning autism" but it took until the mid 1990s for it to be standardized as a diagnosis.[37] Before that, a person with AS was simply considered to be socially awkward or unsociable.

Some research suggests that AS may be as common as one in 250 and it is known that males are more likely to acquire it compared to females at a ratio of eight to one.[38] As AS becomes better understood and recognized, it is believed the number of cases diagnosed will rise.

There is no cure for AS but it can be treated, mostly with a combination of approaches discussed in previous sections relating to ADHD and autism.

For further information and support contact:

Asperger Services Australia – *www.asperger.asn.au*

Autism Spectrum – *www.autismspectrum.org.au*

Autism Aspergers Advocacy Australia – *www.a4.org.au*

REMEMBER...

Children with ADHD, autism and Asperger's syndrome may not enjoy light sensory activities such as tickling. Instead these children love deep pressure holds or moderate to firm holds on both sides of their bodies; in fact they have a strong need for this type of deep touch stimulation which is also a form of affection. These children need you to persist with being playful with them, cuddling them, kissing them and holding their hand. Repetition helps them realize that being playful is important.

Please see related section, *Massage Your Child.*

Dr Jen, what would you do if this was your child?"

I am often asked this question from parents of children with ADHD, autism and Asperger's and I will outline here in point form my approach.

STEP 1

- Spend time getting clear on the vision you have for your child's health. Please examine your intentions and refer to *Power To Parents*.

- Decide to spend less time with people who minimize the effort you are making with your child, such as making comments like "He'll be fine".

- Research ADHD, autism and Asperger's Syndrome.

- Research community networks and support groups for your child.

- Research Leaky Gut Syndrome.

- Learn about self-limiting diets and beneficial digestive enzymes.

- Look through the *Early Signs of a Body out of Balance* and note any area you feel your child might not be 100% well.

- Observe your child for signs of food allergy (as outlined in this chapter).

- Assess if your child is getting enough sleep (as outlined in this chapter).

- Assess their diet for intake of processed foods containing additives, colourings and preservatives (please see *Resource Section* for useful websites).

- Assess how much water they are drinking.

- Consider how much fruit and vegetables they eat in their day.

- Assess how often they use their bowels—please refer to the section *'Poo Tips' For Adults and Children*.

- Calculate how many prescription medications they have had in their lifetime.

- Recall what accidents and falls they have endured.

- Recall your pregnancy and the birth, and consider any possible discomfort or trauma during this time.

- Rate your child's overall health (0 = extremely poor, 10 = fabulous).

- Research and find a recommended chiropractor and other holistic health practitioners who are confident with children.

STEP 2

- See a wellness oriented chiropractor.

- Source practitioner-grade probiotics and EFA supplements—take daily.

- Find a recommended multi-mineral drink or powder.

- Buy a water filter.

- Surround yourself with positive, up-lifting people.

- Be kind to your partner and learn alternate ways to express stress and frustration.

- Prioritize brain foods and good fats every day.

- Commit your child to daily cross-crawling exercise.

- Stock the fridge with an abundance of fresh fruit and vegetables, preferably organic.

- Do an audit of your pantry and throw out as many processed foods as you can.

- Learn how to identify chemicals in the ingredients lists of food items (see *Resource Section* for websites such as "Additive Alert").

- Do an audit of your personal care products, such as shampoos, bubble baths, etc (see *Resource Section* for websites such as "Skin Deep Database").

- Explore new bed-time rituals to facilitate better sleep.

- Engage in some form of physical exercise each day.

- Book yourself on a parenting course or read some parenting books—there's always room for improvement!

- Cut out allergy foods and try an elimination diet—if you need some advice, see a naturopath.

- Meet with parents in similar circumstances who are proactively working with their child.

- Ask for help regularly—commit to weekly 'time out' for you.

- Create laughter in the home with plenty of tickles and commit to expressing more affection.

- Limit your child's television and electronic time.

- Refer to *More 'Feel Good' Moments, Less 'Out-of-Sorts' Moments* (Chapter 1) and learn how neurochemicals influence our child.

- Spend time with your child each day—engaging and connecting with them, free of agendas.

- Explore and discuss functional neurology (balancing the left and right sides of the brain) with your chiropractor.

- Investigate acupuncture and homeopathy.

Is there more I can do?

That's a great question and this chapter is really only the tip of the iceberg. I suggest purchasing books that discuss these health challenges individually and research the specifics of Leaky Gut Syndrome, self-limiting diets and beneficial digestive enzymes. As suggested I would also certainly work hand in hand with community networks.

You may also like to consider the benefit of seeing a chiropractor who specializes in functional neurology. These chiropractic neurologists work specifically on helping balance the left and right sides of the brain. They perform quite distinct techniques to a wellness chiropractor and they usually offer home-based care.

Sometimes parents will visit a chiropractor to help with an acute symptom but will not see the need for on-going chiropractic care for their child. However, I strongly suggest all children—label or no label—need to regularly have their nervous system checked to keep their body and minds functioning well.

Two books related to the topic of functional neurology that I would recommend reading are:

1. *Disconnected Kids: The Groundbreaking Brain Balance Program for Children with Autism, ADHD, Dyslexia, and Other Neurological Disorders* by Dr Robert Melillo (published by Penguin Group).

2. *Your Brain, Your Life* by Dr Robyn Leeder and Dr Kathleen Lawson (published by Health Potential).

There is so much to learn in loving and parenting these beautiful children. Through knowledge and experience we can turn small daily challenges into sweet victories and learn new ways to help our child engage with the world around him.

Conclusion

The underlying message is for parents to proactively help their children authentically engage with the world around them.

We have discussed numerous topics in this book and the underlying message is for parents to proactively help their children authentically engage with the world around them. Most parents will admit that the years seem to 'fly by' when they think of their children growing up. Perhaps the reason they seem to fly is because children learn and change so quickly. In the seeming blink of an eye, your baby is a toddler, and then a child, and then a teenager. The process is indeed a miracle that unfolds rapidly before you.

As parents today we can gather resources, wisdom and skills, all the while remembering that your child's greatest need is YOU. Holding them and loving them. It is your presence (not the activity you share) that helps them feel secure in the world. The only way you can 'slow time down' is to enjoy as many moments as you can. By valuing these precious years and giving your child your fullest attention and love, you will experience a rich and rewarding relationship, no matter what obstacles need to be faced.

At the same time, the love you give to your child is a medicine in its own right; it strengthens all aspects of a child's psychology and physiology, promoting a happiness and vitality that no drug or treatment could ever match.

Every time you delight in your parenting and feel fulfilled by your connection with your child, you can trust that your heart knows that you are helping them to reach their true potential.

I am forever humbled by the power of the body and its self-healing and self-regulating capacity; that is why I believe with the right advice and parameters, parents can indeed take control of their family's health and we can offer children a better future.

Useful Resources

Useful websites:

HEALTH INFORMATION

Additive Alert – Guide To Safer Shopping
www.additivealert.com.au

Food Matters – You Are What You Eat
www.foodmatters.tv

Environmental Working Group
www.ewg.org

Skin Deep Database
www.ewg.org/skindeep

Healthy Child Healthy World
www.healthychild.org

True Food Network
www.truefood.org.au

Dr Joseph Mercola Natural Health Products and Articles
www.drmercola.com

SOURCING A REGISTERED CHIROPRACTOR IN YOUR AREA

Chiropractors' Association of Australia
Ph: 1800 803 665 (Aust. only) / www.chiropractors.asn.au

NZ Chiropractors' Association
www.chiropractic.org.nz

United Chiropractic Association (UK)
www.united-chiropractic.org

International Chiropractors Association (USA)
www.chiropractic.org

International Chiropractic Pediatric Association (USA)
www.icpa4kids.com

International Chiropractor's Association Council
on Chiropractic Pediatrics (USA)
www.icapediatrics.com

American Academy of Pediatarics
www.aap.org

American Chiropractic Association
www.acatoday.org

Canadian Chiropractic Association
www.chiropracticcanada.ca

NATURAL THERAPIES

Australian Natural Therapies Association
Ph: 1800 817 577 (Aust. only) / www.anta.com.au

Australian Acupuncture and Chinese Medicine
Ph: +61 7 3846 5866 / www.acupuncture.org.au

Australian Naturopathic Practitioners Association
Ph: +61 2 9560 7077 / www.anpa.asn.au

Australian Homeopathic Association
Ph: +61 3 5979 1558 or +61 2 9719 2793
www.homeopathyoz.org / www.nhaa.org.au

ADHD AND AUTISM

Autism Australia
www.autismspectrum.org.au

ADHD, Autism and Aspergers in Australia
www.adcet.edu.au/Specific_Impairments/Autism_and_Aspergers.chpx

Defeat Autism Now
www.ariconference.com

MINND
www.mindd.org

Find professionals trained in hemispheric integration therapy
of Functional Neurology
www.carrickinstitite.org

References

INTRODUCTION

1. i. Lee SS, Humphreys KL, Flory K, Liu R, Glass K. Prospective association of childhood attention-deficit/hyperactivity disorder (ADHD) and substance use and abuse/dependence: A meta-analytic review. Clinical Psychology Review 2011;31:328–341
ii. Faraone SV, Sergeant J, Gillberg C, Biederman J. The worldwide prevalence of ADHD: is it an American condition? World Psychiatry June 2003; 2 (2): 104-113.
iii. Martin Whitely. Speed Up and Sit Still. Western Australia Policy Forum. Summary

2. Lantz S Dr. Chemical Free Kids. Australia: Joshua Books; 2009

CHAPTER 1

1. Zimmerman, F. J., Christakis, D. A., Meltzoff, A. N. 2007. *Associations between media viewing and language development in children under age 2 years.* Journal of Pediatrics, 151. 364–368.

2. Bavelier, D., Green, C. S., Dye, M. W. G. 2010. *Children, wired: For better and for worse.* Neuron, 67. 692-701.

3. American Academy of Pediatrics. 2006. AAP - TV AND TODDLERS. [ONLINE] Available at: http://www.aap.org/sections/media/toddlerstv. htm. [Accessed 22 July].

4. Stearns Frederic R. Laughing: physiology, pathophysiology, psychology, pathopsychology, and development. Thomas;1972. Original from the University of Michigan. Digitized.1 Oct 2008

5. Provine Robert R. Quest for Laughter. http://www.umbc.edu/psyc/faculty/provine/book.html

6. Fry, W., & Salameh, W. (Eds.) Handbook of humor and psychotherapy: Advances in the clinical use of humor. Sarasota, FL: Professional Resources. Exchange, Inc;1987.

7. McGhee, P. In Humor: Its Origin and Development. W.H Freeman & CO: San Fransico;1979.

8. Montague, A. Growing young, laughter, play and other life giving basic behavioral needs. An address to the Power of Laughter and Play Conference, Institute for the Advancement of Human Behavior, Stanford, CA:1991.

9. Berk, L. *Neuroendocrine and stress hormone changes during mirthful laughter.* American Journal of Medical Sciences,1989; 298(6), 390—396

10. Nan Allison and Carol Beck. Full and Fullfilled. The Science of Eating to Your Full. Nashville, TN 37204; AB Books: 2000

11. Knickmeyer, R.C., Gouttard, S., et al 2008. *A structural MRI study of human brain development from birth to 2 years.* The Journal of Neuroscience, 28 (47). 12176 –12182.

12. i. Anderson- Peacock, E.S 1996. *Chiropractic adjustments for children.* Can Chiropractor 1(2),21-26
ii. Fallon, J.,2005. The Child patient: *A Matrix for Chiropractic Care.* JCCP. Suppl. 6(3)
iii. C Hawk, M Schneider, R J. Ferrance, E Hewitt, M Van Loon, L Tanis. *Best Practices Recommendations for Chiropractic care in Infants, Children, and Adolescents: Results of a Consensus Process.* JMPT 2009;32:639-647.

13. Linebarger, D. L., Vaala, S. E. 2010. *Screen media and language development in infants and toddlers: An ecological perspective.* Developmental Review, 30. 176-202.

14. Kirkorian, H. L., Pempek, T. A., Murphy, L. A., Schmidt, M. E., Anderson, D. R. 2009. *The Impact of background television on parent–child interaction.* Child Development, 80. 1350-1359. doi: 10.1111/j.1467- 8624.2009.01337.x

15. Griegel-Morris, P., Larson, K, et al, *Incidence of Common Postural Abnormalities in the Cervical, Shoulder and Thoracic Regions and their Association with Pain in Two Age Group of Healthy Subjects.* Physical Therapy. 72(6),425-431.(FHP)

16, 18. Dworak, M,, Schierl, T., Bruns, T., Klaus Struder, H. *Impact of Singular Excessive Computer Game and Television Exposure on Sleep Patterns and Memory Performance of School-aged Children.* Pediatrics 2007; 120(5):978-985.

17. Page, A.S., Cooper, A.R., Griew, P., Jago, R. *Children's Screen Viewing is Related to Psychological Difficulties Irrespective of Physical Activity.* Pediatrics 2010.Published online October 11(doi:10.1542/peds.2010-1154)

19. Kidd, P.M. 2002. *Autism: An extreme challenge to integrative medicine. Part 1: The knowledge base.* Alternative Medicine Review, 7(4). 292-499.

20. McElgunn B. Learning disabilities and the environment: What we know – and how our policies are failing children. Paediatr Child Health 2001;6 (10): 725-727.

21. Bung-Nyun Kim, Soo-Churl Cho et al, *Phthalates Exposure and Attention-Deficit/ Hyperactivity Disorder in School-Age Children.* Biol Psychiatry. 2009.66:958 –963

22. World Health Organisation. Dioxins and their effects on human health Fact sheet N°225 May 2010 http://www.who.int/ mediacentre/factsheets/fs225/en/

23. i.JH. Ford, L MacCormac, J Hiller. PALS (pregnancy and lifestyle study)" association between occupational and environmental exposure to chemicals and reproductive outcome. Mutation Research 313 (1994) 153-164 ii.Sharpe RM, Irvine DS. How strong is the evidence of a link between environmental chemicals and adverse effects on human reproductive health? BMJ 2004; 328(7437):447-51

24. Knickmeyer, R.C., Gouttard, S., et al. *A structural MRI study of human brain development from birth to 2 years.* The Journal of Neuroscience, 2008. 28 (47). 12176 –12182.

25,26. Deakin University Australia. Water - a vital nutrient. 2010. http://www. betterhealth.vic.gov.au/bhcv2/bhcarticles. nsf/pages/water_a_vital_nutrient

27,28,29. Erasmus U. Fats that Heal Fats that Kill. Summertown: Alive Books; 1993.

30,31,32,33,34. Carstens J. *How Safe is Fish?* Cited in: McGuire M. Clean Food Organic. Volume 2. Australia: Custom Publishing; 2006.

35, 36. National Toxicology Program. (2008) Brief on Bisphenol A. [Online]. Available: http://cerhr.niehs.nih.gov/chemicals/ bisphenol/BPADraft BriefVF_04_14_08.pdf [2008].

37. Nehlig A, Boyet S. Dose-response study of caffeine effects on cerebral functional activity with a specific focus on dependence 2000 Elsevier

38. Morris Massey. The People Puzzle. Reston, VA; Reston Publishing Co, Inc:1979.

39. Schore AN Dr. Affect Regulation and the Origin of the Self Study: The Neurobiology of Emotional Development. Cited in: Babette F. Neurobiology says mothers play vital role. News Weekly (Family): July 3; 2004.

40.Babette F. July 3; 2004. Neurobiology - Says Mothers Play Vital Role. News Weekly (Family)

CHAPTER 4

1,2. Manacero, S.A., Marschik, P.B, Nunes, M.L., Einspieler, C. *Is it possible to predict the infant's neurodevelopmental outcome at 14 months of age by means of a single preterm assessment of General Movements?* Early Hum Dev 2011. doi:10.1016/j.earlhumdev.2011.06.013

3. Gutmann, G. 1987. *Blocked atlantal nerve syndrome in babies and infants.* Manuelle Medezin, 25: 5-10.

4. Frymann, V.M., Springall, P. 1992. *Effect of osteopathic medical management on neurological development in children.* JAOA, 92:729.

5. Anderson- Peacock, E.S 1996. *Chiropractic adjustments for children.* Can Chiropractor 1(2),21-26

6. i.Epigenetics, Evolution, Endocrine Disruption, Health, and Disease Endocrinology 147(6) (Supplement):S4 –S10. 2006 The Endocrine Society doi: 10.1210/en.2005-1122
ii. Lillycrop, K.A. 2011. Epigenetics. Effect of maternal diet on the epigenome: implications for human metabolic disease. Proc nutr Soc.2011, Feb:70(1):64-72

7,8,9.Executive Summary Environmental Working Group, July 14, 2005. Body Burden — The Pollution in Newborns: A benchmark investigation of industrial chemicals, pollutants and pesticides in umbilical cord blood http://www.ewg.org/ reports/bodyburden2/execsumm.php

10. Epigenetics, Evolution, Endocrine Disruption, Health, and Disease Endocrinology 147(6) (Supplement):S4 –S10. 2006 The Endocrine Society doi: 10.1210/en.2005-1122

11.Rowe, K.S., Rowe, K.L. 1994. Synthetic food colouring and behaviour: A dose response effect in a double-blind, placebo-controlled, repeated measures study. Journal of Paediatrics, 125:691-698.

12. i. Lipski E PhD. Digestive Wellness For Children. Laguna Beach; Basic Health Publications: 2006.
ii. Washington State Department of Health, Division of Environmental Health, Office of Drinking Water. "Disinfection Byproducts." http://www.doh.wa.gov/ehp/dw/Publications/disinfection_byproducts.htm

13. i. Walker Smith JA. Diagnostic Criteria for Gastrointestinal Food Allergy in Childhood. Clin Exp Allergy. 1995;25:20-22.
ii. Brostoff J Dr. Gamlin L. The Complete guide to Food Allergy and Intolerance. London: Bloomsbury Publishing;1992.

14,15. Galland L MD. Super-immunity for Kids. New York: Dell Publishing Group; 1989.

16. Meeker, W.C., Halderman, S. Chiropractic: A profession at the crossroads of mainstream and alternative medicine. Ann Intern Med. 2002; 136:216-217.

CHAPTER 5

1.i. Lee SS, Humphreys KL, Flory K, Liu R, Glass K. Prospective association of childhood attention-deficit/hyperactivity disorder (ADHD) and substance use and abuse/dependence: A meta-analytic review. Clinical Psychology Review 2011;31:328–341
ii. Faraone SV, Sergeant J, Gillberg C, Biederman J. The worldwide prevalence of ADHD: is it an American condition? World Psychiatry June 2003; 2 (2): 104-113.
iii. Martin Whitely. Speed Up and Sit Still. Western Australia Policy Forum. Summary

2. Dengate S. *Food and Behaviour.* Informed Choice: Spring; Vol 4(3) 2004.

3. Lipski E PhD. Digestive Wellness For Children. Laguna Beach; Basic Health Publications: 2006.

4. i.Schnoll R, Burshteyn D, Cea-Aravena *Nutrition in the Treatment of Attention-Deficit Hyperactivity Disorder: A Neglected but Important Aspect.* J. Appl Psychophysiol Biofeedback 2003 Mar;28(1):63-75.
ii. Richardson AJ, Puri BK. *The potential role of fatty acids in attention-deficit/hyperactivity disorder.* Prostaglandins, Leukotrienes and Essential Fatty Acids. 2000; 63:79-87

5,6. Rowe KS. Rowe KL. *Synthetic Food Colouring and Behaviour: a Dose Response Effect in a Double-blind, Placebo-controlled, Repeated Measures Study.* J Paediat. 1994;125:691-698.

7,8. Stratham B. (2005). The Chemical Maze-Your Guide to Food Additives and Cosmetic Ingredients [Online]. Available: www.thechemicalmaze.com.baby [2005].

9. The Centre for Science in the Public Interest website, "CSPI Says Food Dyes Pose Rainbow of Risks", June 29, 2010 www.cspinet.org/new/201006291.html

10. May Loo. Integrative Medicine for Children (First Edition), 2009, Chapter 13: Attention-Deficit Hyperactivity Disorder. pp 178-192. Saunders.

11. Kozielec T, Starobrat-Hermelin B. *Assessment of magnesium levels in children with attention deficit hyperactivity disorder (ADHD)* Magnes Res. 1997 Jun;10(2):143-8.

12. Richardson AJ, Puri BK. *The potential role of fatty acids in attention-deficit/hyperactivity disorder.* Prostaglandins, Leukotrienes and Essential Fatty Acids. 2000; 63:79-87

13. Bilicia M, Yıldırıma F, Kandilb S, Bekaroglua M, Yıldırmıs O, Degerc O, Ulgena M, Yıldırand A, Aksub H. Double-blind, placebo-controlled study of zinc sulfate in the treatment of attention deficit hyperactivity disorder. Progress in Neuro-Psychopharmacology & Biological Psychiatry 2004; 28: 181– 190.

14. Harding KL, Judah RD, Gant CE. *Outcome-Based Comparison of Ritalin® versus Food-Supplement Treated Children with AD/HD.* Alternative Medicine Review 2003; 8(3): 319-330.

15. Goldbeck L, Schmid K. *Effectiveness of autogenic relaxation training on children and adolescents with behavioral and emotional problems.* J Am Acad Child Adolesc Psychiatry. 2003 Sep;42(9):1046-54.

16. Brzozowski WE, Walter T. *The Effects of Chiropractic Treatment on Students With Learning and Behavioral Impairments Due to Neurological Dysfunction.* Paper presented at the Annual Conference of the Association of Children with Learning Disabilities (12th, Texas)

17. Cuthbert SC, Barras M. *Developmental Delay Syndromes: Psychometric Testing Before and After Chiropractic Treatment of 157 children.* J Manipulative Physiol Ther 2009; 32:660-669.

18,19. i. Ritalin-SR Medication Guide, rev. 4/2007: www.fda.gov/downloads/Drugs/DrugSafety/ucm089095.pdf www.nimh.nih.gov/health/publications/medications/medications.pdf.
ii. Physicians' Desk Reference, 58th ed. Montvale, NJ: Thomson PDR, 2004. Iii. Johns Hopkins Medicine, Health Alerts, "Heart Attack: Symptoms and Remedies": www.johnshopkinshealthalerts.com/symptoms_remedies/heart_attack/83-1.html#3 (2008).

20. Merson, J. 2002. The wild ones. Good Weekend, The Age Magazine, May 11.

21. Matson, J.L., Kozlowski, A.M. 2010. The increasing prevalence of autism spectrum disorders. Research in Autism Spectrum Disorders. http://dx.doi.org 10.1016/j.rasd.2010.06.004.

22. Llaneza DC, DeLuke SV, Batista M, Crawley JN, Christodulu KV, Frye CA. *Communication, interventions, and scientific advances in autism: A commentary.* Physiology & Behavior 2010; 100: 268-276.

23. O'Reilly, B., Smith, S. The Australian Autism Handbook: Jane Curry Publishing; 2008.

24,25. Kidd, P.M. 2002. *Autism, an extreme challenge to integrative medicine. Part 1: The knowledge base.* Alternative Medicine Review, 7(4): 292-499.

26. i.Rojas Wahl, R.U. 2004. *Could oxytocin administration during labor contribute to autism and related behavioral disorders? A look at the literature.* Medical Hypotheses, 63: 456-460.
ii. Modahl C, Fein D, Waterhouse L, Newton N. *Does oxytocin deficiency mediate social deficits in autism?* J Autism Dev Disord 1992;22:449-51
iii. Ferguson J, Young L, Insel T. *The neuroendocrine basis of social recognition.* Front Neuroendocrin 2002;23: 200-24

27. i. Insel T, O'Brien D, Leckman J. *Oxytocin, vasopressin and autism: Is there a connection?* Biol Psychiatr 1999;45: 145-57
ii.Insel T, O'Brien D, Leckman J. *Oxytocin,*

vasopressin and autism: Is there a connection? Biol Psychiatr 1999;45: 145-57.
iii.Insel T, Young L. *The neurobiology of attachment.* Nat Rev: Neurosci 2001;2:129-36.

28. Guastella AJ, Einfeld EL, Gray, K, Rinehart N, Tonge B, Lambert TJ, Hickie IB (April 2010). *"Intranasal oxytocin improves emotion recognition for youth with autism spectrum disorders".* Biological Psychiatry 67 (7): 692-4. doi:10.1016/j.biopsych.2009.09.020. PMID 19897177.

29. Jacob S, Brune CW, Carter CS, Leventhal BL, Lord C, Cook EH (April 2007). *"Association of the oxytocin receptor gene (OXTR) in Caucasian children and adolescents with autism".* Neuroscience Letters 417 (1): 6-9. doi:10.1016/j.neulet.2007.02.001. PMC 2705963. PMID 17383819.

31. Wermter AK, Kamp-Becker I, Hesse P, Schulte-Körne G, Strauch K, Remschmidt H (September 2009). *"Evidence for the involvement of genetic variation in the oxytocin receptor gene (OXTR) in the etiology of autistic disorders on high-functioning level".* American Journal of Medical Genetics. Part B, Neuropsychiatric Genetics 153B (2): 629-39. doi:10.1002/ajmg.b.31032. PMID 19777562.

32, 33. Kinney, D.K., Munir, K.M., Crowley, D.J., Miller, A.M. *Prenatal stress and risk for autism.* Neuroscience and Biobehavioral Reviews, 2008. 32: 1519- 1532.

34. Adamsa J.B., Romdalvika, J. Sadagopa Ramanujamb, V.M., Legotorb, M.S. 2006. *Mercury, lead and zinc in baby teeth of children with autism versus controls.* Journal of Toxicology and Environmental Health, Part A, 70(12): 1046-1051

35. Fallon, J. 2005. *Could one of the most widely prescribed antibiotics amoxicillin/clavulanate augmentin be a risk factor for autism?* Medical Hypotheses, 64: 312-315.

36. Fallon, J. 2005. *Is autism a brain disorder or a gut disorder?* Today's Chiropractic.

37. Lyons V, Fitzgerald M. *Did Hans Asperger have Asperger Syndrome?.* J Autism Dev Disord 2007 37 (10):2020-1. doi:10.1007/s10803-007-03824

38. Osborne L. American Normal : The Hidden World of Asperger Syndrome. Copernicus; 2002.

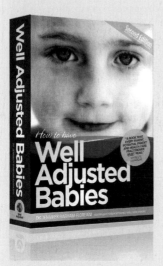